Policy Studies in Ageing

One of the greatest achievements of the twentieth century has been to add over 20 years to the average life expectancy (at birth) of British people. To survive into 'old age' is no longer a bonus for a small minority of people but an experience common to the majority. Retired people now constitute one-sixth of the population of the United Kingdom. *Policy Studies in Ageing* is a series of monographs which seeks to promote substantial contributions to public debate about policy issues which affect older members of society. The subjects to be covered in this series include not only the traditional concerns of policy-makers with health, housing and social services for older age groups, but also wider aspects of policy such as retirement, income maintenance, education and the use of leisure. These monographs are published by the Centre for Policy on Ageing, a registered charity established in 1947 to promote better policies for older people, under the overall direction of the Centre's Advisory Council.

Policy Studies in Ageing is aimed at a wide readership amongst those in central and local government, the health authorities and voluntary bodies who are responsible for the formulation of policy or its implementation in practice. The series will also be of interest to those studying social policy or administration in universities and polytechnics and, it is hoped, to all who take an intelligent interest in the quality of their own later years.

Professor R A B Leaper, *University of Exeter*
Chairman, Advisory Council, Centre for Policy on Ageing

Other titles in the series
Alison Norman, *Mental illness in old age: meeting the challenge.* Policy Studies in Ageing no. 1, 1982

Eric Midwinter, *Age is opportunity: education and older people.* Policy Studies in Ageing no. 2, 1982

Alison Norman, *Triple jeopardy: growing old in a second homeland.* Policy Studies in Ageing no. 3, 1985

Eric Midwinter, *The wage of retirement: the case for a new pensions policy.* Policy Studies in Ageing no. 4, 1985

Alan Norton, Bryan Stoten and Hedley Taylor, *Councils of care: planning a local government strategy for older people.* Policy Studies in Ageing no. 5, 1986

Hedley Taylor, *Growing old together: elderly owner-occupiers and their housing.* Policy Studies in Ageing no. 6, 1986

Policy Studies in Ageing
no 7

Severe

dementia:

the provision of

longstay care

Alison Norman

Centre for Policy on Ageing

First published 1987 by the
Centre for Policy on Ageing
25–31 Ironmonger Row
London EC1V 3QP

© 1987 Centre for Policy on Ageing

All rights reserved. No part of this publication may be reproduced or transmitted, in any form or by any means, without the prior consent of the copyright owner.

ISBN 0 904 139 52 2

Printed in Great Britain by Henry Ling Ltd., at the Dorset Press, Dorchester, Dorset.

Contents

Foreword

This study is not formal 'research'. The brief from the Mental Health Division of the Department of Health and Social Security was to visit and describe 15 specialist establishments with no more than 30 beds which were seeking to provide high-quality longstay care for dementia sufferers (the total was later reduced to 14). Each establishment was to be visited several times during the day and night over a 24 hour period and described in terms of building design, physical and mental dependency of residents, regime, activities, staff levels, staff training, assessment procedures, and so on. Opinions concerning the nature and quality of the service offered were to be sought from all types of staff, relevant local professionals, relatives of residents and, so far as possible, from the residents themselves. The resulting case studies inevitably reflect the author's personal predilection and perceptions, although the value judgements made are based on the principles of good care set out in *Home life: a code of practice for residential care*[1]. The aim has not been to achieve total objectivity or to compare the establishments on some sort of scale, but rather to describe each one in terms which will enable service providers to examine their own practices and future plans in the light of these initiatives.

The study falls into five main sections.

1. A short introductory chapter explains the nature of dementia and comments on the debate concerning care for sufferers who can no longer be maintained in their own homes. It argues that specialist longstay care is essential for some people in this category.

2. This section summarises data on statutory and private specialist provision in the United Kingdom obtained from responses to questionnaires sent to every health and social services authority in the UK. Its main objective is to set the study in the context of present provision and future trends. (This was not part of the DHSS brief but was considered to be essential for the report to justify its status as a CPA Policy Study).

3. The findings from the 14 detailed case studies are analysed under a range of headings in order to bring out examples of interesting and innovative practice and describe the advantages or disadvantages of different forms of provision.

4. The 14 establishments are described individually. This inevitably makes for somewhat indigestible reading but the detail provided is essential for service providers who want to make practical use of the study.

5. The report concludes with a brief summary of key aspects of good practice and suggestions for further research.

There are many popular euphemisms as well as various technical terms for the condition which the report refers to as 'dementia' and which is described at the beginning of the introductory chapter. Terms in common non-technical use include 'elderly mentally infirm' (EMI) 'elderly severely mentally infirm' (ESMI) 'confused' and 'mentally frail'. However, all these terms are also frequently used with reference to people suffering confusional states which are not caused by brain cell loss. The term 'dementia' has therefore been used throughout the report, in spite of the stigma which it may be felt to carry.

A similar stigma is also often felt to be associated with the words 'psychogeriatric' and 'psychogeriatrician'. However, as I have said in an earlier study:

'It seems defeatist to allow perfectly good and convenient words to go out of use because they are subject to misuse by the ignorant. The World Health Organisation in 1972 stated that psychogeriatrics is a branch of psychiatry concerned with all the mental disorders of old age, but particularly with those that first emerge as significant at the age of 65 years. Psychogeriatrics is concerned with the various forms of mental disorder in old age, their epidemiology, origin, prevention, development and treatment.'[2]

It is in this broad sense that these words are used in this report.

The limitations of the English language also make it necessary to say a word about the use of pronouns. The lack of a neutral pronoun in the third person singular forces any writer either to use one gender throughout, or to resort to the clumsy 'he or she', or to make an arbitrary choice. Reluctantly, I have settled for the third option, as being the least obtrusive. Thus, doctors are 'he' and patients, social workers, nurses and care staff are 'she' except where the context demands otherwise. Inevitably this usage reinforces stereotypes and readers are asked to keep in mind the many female psychiatrists and male nurses and residential care staff who are contributing in this field and the many elderly men who suffer from dementia.

Finally, readers will note that, contrary to usual practice in DHSS-sponsored research, the report identifies both the establishments described in the case studies and many individual informants. One reason for this is that identification enables readers to judge the relevance of the information to their own situation and, if they wish to do so, to follow it up with personal contact. It thus adds considerably to the practical value of the report. There is also a danger that unless individual informants are identified by name, their views and practices may be ascribed to their successors or to someone with a similar role in the locality concerned. Since they were asked to discuss their work or give their opinions in a personal capacity it seemed only proper that this should be acknowledged personally.

Inevitably, identification carries with it the risk of misrepresentation. Every effort has been made to check that the account given in the report accurately reflects the situation as it was at the time of the visit or interview. However, summary accounts of complex situations or conversations are bound to be misleading to some extent and in such a rapidly changing field descriptions which were accurate at the time of writing may well be out of date even by the date of publication. Readers are asked to be aware of this and to check with the source if they want to obtain a fully up-to-date picture.

REFERENCES
1. *Home life: a code of practice for residential care.* Centre for Policy on Ageing, London, 1984.
2. A Norman, *Mental illness in old age: meeting the challenge.* Centre for Policy on Ageing, London, 1982.

Alison Norman
November 1986

Acknowledgements

Grateful thanks are due to the Mental Health Division of the Department of Health and Social Security, which commissioned this report, and to the Research Management Division of the Department for constant support and helpful advice while it was being carried out. Thanks are also due to the residents, members of staff and professional associates of the establishments included in the case studies for their generous co-operation and their detailed and helpful comments on the draft. I am also grateful to the Social Services Departments of Birmingham, Cambridgeshire, Wiltshire, Sheffield and Stockport, the Northern and Eastern Health and Social Service Boards in Northern Ireland, the Health Authorities of Exeter, Central Manchester and Peterborough, the Borders Health Board, the Church of Scotland's Board of Social Responsibility, and the proprietors of Highland House in Hunstanton, Kilncroft Rest Home in Hastings and R & M Homes in Southport for permission to include their establishments in this study.

Amongst my colleagues at CPA, I would particularly like to thank Jeanne Isaacs who provided invaluable assistance in analysing returns to the questionnaires and setting-up appointments, also Nancy Klein and Joy Ewer who typed and re-typed the drafts, and Gabrielle Preston who copy-edited the final text and saw the report through to publication.

Alison Norman

Relevant CPA publications

Alison Norman, *Rights and risk: a discussion document on civil liberty in old age.* National Corporation for the Care of Old People, London, 1980.

Alison Norman, *Mental health and illness in old people's homes.* Homes Advice Broadsheet 6, Centre for Policy on Ageing, London, 1980.

Alison Norman, *Mental illness in old age: meeting the challenge.* Policy Studies in Ageing no. 1, Centre for Policy on Ageing, London, 1982.

Alison Norman, *Bricks and mortals: design and lifestyle in old people's homes.* CPA Reports no. 4, Centre for Policy on Ageing, London, 1984.

Home life: a code of practice for residential care. Report of a Working Party sponsored by the DHSS and convened by CPA under the chairmanship of Kina, Lady Avebury. Centre for Policy on Ageing, London, 1984.

Brenda Hooper, *Home ground: how to select and get the best out of staff.* Centre for Policy on Ageing, London, 1984.

Terri Donovan and Deirdre Wynne-Harley, *Not a nine-to-five job: staffing and management in private and voluntary residential care homes.* CPA Reports no. 7, Centre for Policy on Ageing, London, 1986.

Glossary of abbreviations

ADS	Alzeimers Disease Society
CAPE	Clifton Assessment Procedures for the Elderly
CCTESW	Central Council for Training and Education in Social Work
CRBRS	Crichton Royal Behavioural Rating Scale
CQSW	Certificate of qualification in social work
CPN	Community psychiatric nurse
CSS	Certificate in social service
DDD	Demonstration Development District
DGH	District general hospital
DHSS	Department of Health and Social Security
DMHE	Department of Mental Health for the Elderly
EMI	Elderly mentally infirm
ESMI	Elderly severely mentally infirm
GP	General practitioner
HA	Health authority
LA	Local authority
NHS	National Health Service
OIC	Officer in charge (of a home)
OT	Occupational therapist
RMN	Registered mental nurse
RNMH	Registered nurse of the mentally handicapped
RO	Reality orientation
SEN	State enrolled nurse
SIP	Specialising in practice
SRN	State registered nurse
SSD	Social services department
WTE	Whole time equivalent

Part III accommodation—Residential homes provided by local authorities under Part III of the National Assistance Act, 1948.

1 The need for specialist care

The term 'dementia' is used in this report to cover the various forms of disease which progressively destroy the cells of the brain and thus cause de-mentia—literally 'loss of mind'. Dementia must not be confused with functional illness such as depression or paranoid delusional states, disorientation caused by social isolation or by apathy resulting from bereavement and loss of role; nor with reversible confusional states caused by physical illness, inappropriate medication or sudden environmental change. Still less should dementia be confused with the ordinary forgetfulness of old age.

The most common form of dementia is usually called Alzheimer's disease or 'senile dementia of the Alzheimer type' (SDAT) but this in itself is an umbrella term for a syndrome which includes wide variations in age of onset, speed of deterioration and effect on personality. Another common form is multi-infarct dementia which is caused by repeated mini-strokes which cut off the blood supply to the brain and thus kill brain tissue. But, whatever the cause, true dementia is a very distressing illness both to the sufferers and their carers. The early symptoms affect short-term memory, personal initiative and the quantity and quality of constructive activity. Usual hobbies and skills are neglected and conversation becomes stultified, stereotyped and repetitive. Previous personality traits may become exaggerated or may be reversed to quite untypical behaviour. As the disease progresses, the effects of memory loss become more apparent. Sufferers may literally be 'living in the past' since that is where their remaining long-term memory has taken them, and therefore identify those around them with parents or siblings rather than children or grandchildren. They may struggle to escape from a home which has become unfamiliar to go back to the home of their childhood. They may cause havoc by trying to put coal on the electric fire or an electric kettle on the stove. Speech and muscle co-ordination may be affected and finally lower brain functions such as conscious control of the sphincter and bladder muscles and the capacity to swallow may go. Indeed, as R L Symonds starkly says in a classic article:

'Dementia is a dismantling of the human being, starting at the most organised and complex part and proceeding with the failure of the central nervous system components. It involves brain cell death; it progressively involves lower parts of the central nervous system, so that if no other illnesses were to supervene it would cause death. It follows that dementia is a form of dying.'[1]

Many dementia sufferers are cared for by relatives or neighbours, often at great personal cost. It is basic to the whole content of this report that such caring must be backed-up by comprehensive and individually planned support services in the form of an accessible psychogeriatric team; respite and relief admission facilities; specialist day care and home help provision; an incontinent laundry service and skilled social work[2]. But, given our present level of skill and resources, there is a point at which some people suffering from a dementing illness simply cannot be given the 24-hour care which they need without causing intolerable stress to their carers. When this happens they may not be acceptable in 'ordinary' residential care so that 'community care' creates its own demand for specialist care.

If service provision is to be properly planned, a more up-to-date and sophisticated epidemiological study of the incidence of dementia than that done in Newcastle in the 1960's is urgently needed[3]. It is however clear that the Newcastle researchers were right in finding that incidence rises very steeply with age. They estimated 2.8 per cent of sufferers in the 71–74 age group, 5.5 per cent in the 75–79 age group and 22 per cent in the over 80's. The number of people in the UK aged 80 plus is expected to increase by nearly 300,000 between the year of writing (1986) and 2001. If 22 per cent are dementia sufferers, there will be in increase of 66,000 cases in this age group alone and even if 90 per cent of them can be looked after in ordinary housing or integrated residential care (an optimistic estimate) we will need 6,600 *more* longstay beds for dementia sufferers in their 80's by 2001 than we have at present, and current provision is inadequate both in quantity and quality. These figures drive home both the importance and the urgency of getting our plans and our models for longstay provision right as quickly as possible.

It is important to begin by acknowledging that institutional care of any kind has a very poor image. This arises from its long association with the workhouse; the horror stories recounted in such publications as *Sans everything*[4] and *The last refuge*[5]; the well publicised scandals relating to practices in the longstay wards of psychiatric hospitals with subsequent official enquiries; and the fear of exploitation arising from the recent explosion of private care. Real evidence of poor provision in every sector is fuelled by guilt and sensationalism so that even the battle to improve and monitor standards has the effect of highlighting bad practice. At the same time 'community care' in the sense of providing support to people in their own homes, has become commonly accepted as the most desirable option and the advocacy of 'community care' has tended to carry with it a corresponding blackening of the institutional alternatives.

All this has a knock-on effect both on the resources devoted to longstay care and on the prestige of those who provide it so that a vicious circle of inadequate resources, low prestige and poor quality of care is all too easily established. As CPA has said when discussing longstay psychiatric hospital provision:

'There is a real and painful conflict between devoting resources to acute treatment and providing decent care for long-term patients. And as longstay care loses out and becomes more and more third rate, the guilt we feel at poor provision becomes allied to the conviction that longstay psychiatric hospital care is a last resort, to be avoided at all costs. Given this conviction, how can we genuinely respect those who staff this last resort? Society seems to be telling the staff of our longstay wards, "Make us feel good by caring on our behalf, but do not expect the resources to do it properly or social respect and prestige for doing it at all"'[6].

Associated with, and arising from this poor image of institutional care is a different argument. This recognises that there will always be people who cannot continue to live in a domestic setting and that we need to stop bemoaning the dangers of longstay care and set about eliminating these by working to provide a lifestyle which recognises the rights of residents and maximises the 'normality' of their existence. CPA's own study *Rights and risk*[7]; the publications of the now defunct Personal Social Services Council; the work of researchers at the North London Polytechnic[8]; various studies from the King's Fund Centre[9]; and the officially recognised *Home life: a code of practice for residential care*[10], provide some benchmarks in this process, and further effective work has been done in the different but relevant field of mental handicap. Here Kushlick's pioneering teamwork in Wessex, the Campaign for Mentally Handicapped People (CMH) and the King's Fund Centre have done a great deal to promote concepts of involvement, 'normalisation' and opportunity for choice and self-determination. CMH's report *The principal of normalisation*[11] has much to say to people working in the field of residential care for the elderly in general, and elderly people with dementia in particular and their training materials can usefully be adapted for this purpose. Some work on transferring and defining the principles involved has already begun in the King's Fund project paper *Living well into old age*[12]. This defines the human dignities and values which are common to everyone and spells out the implications of making the defence of these a reality for frontline staff and service providers. The document poses a series of key questions which providers of both domiciliary and residential services need to ask themselves, together with a further checklist for strategic managers and planners. It is intended to be used as a focus for the work of local planning and monitoring groups. It has been used in the analysis of the case studies provided in Chapter 3 of this report.

Many people who would subscribe to the basic principles of good residential care outlined in *Home life* and other publications[13] remain convinced that they cannot be adequately practised in settings which segregate dementia-sufferers from other dependent elderly people. They argue that *all* elderly people in residential care have the same basic needs and that it is unjust to cut some of them off from the enjoyment of equal status and facilities because of a 'label' of 'dementia' which may be inappropriate because of mis-diagnosis, or be exacerbated by socially-induced disorientation, and which may fluctuate in severity from day to day. This argument can be challenged on two grounds. In the first place, it almost always refers to integration or segregation within local authority homes or the private sector and ignores the much more severe segregation which takes place in the relegation of those who are considered unsuitable for ordinary residential care to the longstay wards of psychiatric hospitals. It is widely acknowledged that many (some would argue all), of the patients in longstay specialist hospital wards could be cared for in properly staffed and equipped specialist homes, but it may not be possible to care for them in ordinary homes without cruelty to the mentally-alert residents and intolerable strain on the staff. In the second place, advocates of 'integration' assume that poor assessment procedures will always result in 'misplacement' and that specialist care inevitably offers a quality of life which is poorer than that likely to be experienced by dementia sufferers in an 'ordinary' residential home. The examples provided in this study show that these assumptions are not necessarily valid.

In this debate Michael Meacher's study *Taken for a ride*[14] is often cited as conclusive evidence against 'segregation', frequently one suspects, by people who have not read it. Though published in 1972, the research appears to have been done in 1967 when there was little in the way of general awareness of the complex aetiology of confusional symptoms, and assessment techniques were in their infancy. It looked at three specialist homes 'in which confused old people were the majority or substantial minority' and which were chosen from a list supplied by the Ministry of Health. One was a large isolated old manor house with minimal modern facilities, run by a voluntary agency; one was a modern purpose-built local authority Part III home with an open-plan design; and one was a new wing of an old workhouse. All catered for a very wide mix of mental disability, (one-fifth of the residents in one of the homes were classified as subnormal) and they evidently included what would now be considered a disastrously high percentage of people who got there by misadventure or lack of alternative placement.

Meacher's methodology was based on interviews with residents, watching daily routine and the use of a 'confusion scale' devised by himself. His arguments rest on his assumption that separatist regimes *inevitably* generate the practices he observed, such as dumping people into care without discussion or explanation (being 'taken for a ride'); infantilising procedures; heavy sedation; physical restraint; ritualised questions; and 'similar devices'. Thus Meacher's book is a pioneer in the use of observation as a research tool and is a mine of awful examples of bad practice, but it does not provide the foundation for any attack on the sort of specialist care described in this study.

Another important piece of research in this field which is often cited in support of 'integrated care' was undertaken by a team in Manchester in 1981[15]. However this study was concerned with issues relating to the management of a mixed group of residents and the nature of a 'desirable balance' of lucid and confused residents, and did not attempt to compare mixed and specialist residential care. (Manchester does not have any specialist homes.) The study concludes that about 30 per cent of people suffering from moderate or severe dementia 'can be tolerated' in ordinary homes, and these can offer considerable advantages for confused residents in terms of greater stimulation and a more 'homely' environment than can be provided in 'specialist institutions', by which the authors mean longstay hospital wards. Valuable as the Manchester study is in relation to the management of a 'mix' of disability, it therefore has little to say about the pros and cons of specialist residential care for people who suffer from severe dementia allied to behavioural difficulties[15].

Finally, mention must be made of a detailed study carried out by the Social Work Service of the DHSS (now the Social Services Inspectorate)[16]. The inspectors looked at 20 local authority homes which included specialist units, ordinary homes with specialist wings, and homes providing integrated care. They visited each home over a 24-hour period, as the author did in this study, and came to similar conclusions and recommendations about key issues of good practice. However, their report makes no attempt to compare the quality of care received by residents in the specialist homes and wings (which were not described or identified) with that received in the integrated homes. We therefore still lack any serious comparison between integrated and specialist care, and, apart from a detailed and far-sighted discussion of design considerations in this field by the Wyvern Partnership working with the Social Services Unit at the University of Birmingham[17], there has been very little study at all of specialist care in a non-hospital setting.

We must move beyond the sterile argument as to whether specialist care is or is not a 'good thing' to the issue of how the care of *any* person can be provided in a way which acknowledges both *their* worth and dignity, and the worth, dignity and skills of the staff who provide that care. There will always be a 'mix' of mental ability in the residents of 'ordinary' old peoples' homes, and much more needs to be done to support and train staff in recognising and coping with functional and organic mental illness, as CPA has strongly argued in the past[18]. But specialist care will also be needed. This report demonstrates that if it is properly provided by staff who are encouraged to see 'special' as a symbol of excellence and not of segregation, specialist units can become models of good practice, resource centres for community-based carers, and a public acknowledgement of the individuality and dignity of every person for whom our society is responsible, no matter how disabled in mind and body they may be.

REFERENCES
1. R L Symonds, Dementia as an experience. *Nursing Times*, 17, 40, 30 Sept 1981, 1708-1710.

2. E Levin, I Sinclair and P Gorbach, *The supporters of confused elderly persons at home.* National Institute for Social Work, London, 1983.

3. Summarised in Office of Health Economics, *Dementia in old age.* Office of Health Economics, London, 1979.

4. B Robb, *Sans everything: a case to answer.* Nelson, London, 1967.

5. P Townsend, *The last refuge.* Routledge & Kegan Paul, London, 1962.

6. A Norman, *Mental illness in old age: meeting the challenge.* Centre for Policy on Ageing, London, 1982.

7. A Norman, *Rights and risk: a discussion document on civil liberty in old age.* National Corporation for the Care of Old People, London, 1980.

8. See for example, Paul Ward, *Quality of life in residential care.* PSSC, London 1980; Phyllis Willmott, *Do you live in a residential home? Do you work in a residential home? Do you have a relative in a residential home?* PSSC, London, 1979; PSSC, *Living and working in residential homes.* Interim Report of a Working Group, PSSC, London, 1975.

9. See for example, King Edward's Hospital Fund for London, *Living well into old age: applying principles of good practice to services for elderly people with severe mental disabilities.* King Edward's Hospital Fund, London, 1985 (unpublished); King's Fund Centre, *Long term and community care.* KFC 80/6, King's Fund Centre, London, 1980.

10. *Home life: a code of practice for residential care.* Centre for Policy on Ageing, London, 1984.

11. A Tyne, *The principle of normalisation: a foundation for effective services.* Campaign for Mentally Handicapped People, London, 1981.

12. *Living well into old age,* op. cit.

13. See for example *Home life,* op. cit. and other relevant publications listed on page xxiii.

14. M Meacher, *Taken for a ride.* Longman, London, 1972.

15. G Evans *et al, The management of mental and physical impairment in non-specialist residential homes for the elderly.* University Hospital of South Manchester, Psychogeriatric Unit, Manchester, 1981.

16. Department of Health and Social Security, Social Services Inspectorate, *Inspection of local authority care for elderly mentally disordered people.* Department of Health and Social Security, London, 1985.

17. Wyvern Partnership, Architects, and Social Services Unit, University of Birmingham, *A report on the provision of residential accommodation for the elderly mentally infirm.* Department of Health and Social Security, London, 1977.

18. Norman, *Mental illness in old age,* op. cit.

19. *Mental health and illness in old people's homes.* Homes Advice Broadsheet 6, Centre for Policy on Ageing, London, 1980.

2 Present and planned provision: the broad picture

Introduction

Although the bulk of this report is concerned with care in individual establishments, it seemed important to set them in context by trying to obtain a broad national view of present provision and future plans in this field. Because CPA's remit covers the whole of the United Kingdom, this enquiry was extended to Northern Ireland, Scotland and Wales. In each case, informants who were in a position to discuss the overall situation were visited and asked to provide any information which they thought relevant, and questionnaires covering statutory and non-statutory provision were sent to all health and local authorities. With the help of a final 'telephone round-up' an almost 100 per cent response was obtained.

The questionnaire to health authority administrators asked them how many longstay beds for 'EMI patients, excluding those who had grown old in hospital', their authority provided for or maintained in traditional psychiatric hospitals; geriatric hospitals; district general hospitals and small localised specialist units; and whether any establishments in the last category were joint-funded with the local authority. Further open-ended questions asked them to summarise their authority's policy, if any, in this area; to recommend any establishment which they thought to be of particular interest and to make any other observations they wished. (It did not seem practicable to ask them to distinguish between patients suffering from dementing illness and those suffering from other age-related mental disorders and, in the event, accurate data proved difficult to obtain even on this generalised basis.) In a separate questionnaire NHS registration officers were asked to state: how many private nursing homes specialising in the care of dementia sufferers they had registered; how many of these were registered as mental nursing homes and how many were considered to be 'specialist in practice' (SIP) though they were not registered as such; and details of the beds provided in each category. The registration officers were also asked their views on the ability of the private nursing-home sector to provide good care for this client group and to recommend any homes which were thought to offer an exceptional standard of care.

In the residential field, local authority social services departments were asked to state how many specialist longstay beds for dementia sufferers they provided in specialist homes or wings, their policy in this field, and to recommend any exceptional Part III provision. Their registration officers were asked questions similar to those put to their NHS counterparts.

It has not been possible, in a section which is subsidiary to the main report, to include a full analysis of the replies to these four questionnaires, but a good outline of the responses is given below.

A national survey

England
Table 1 gives an idea of the overall pattern of specialist provision in England although, for reasons given below, the figures for NHS traditional hospital beds must be taken with some caution. Of a total of approximately 31,000 specialist beds it seems that the NHS provides about 79 per cent, the local authorities 12 per cent and the private and voluntary sector eight per cent. Well over half of this provision is in traditional psychiatric hospitals. These figures are broken down and discussed further below.

National Health Service provision
Table 2 represents an attempt to summarise NHS provision for dementia sufferers in England but the figures cannot be taken as definitive, particularly in relation to traditional psychiatric hospitals. This is because some authorities make no administrative distinction between provision for organic illness, recent functional illness and longstanding psychotic disorder, or do not separate long-term and short-term facilities. Also, the abolition of the area health authorities has left a large number of districts dependent on beds in traditional hospitals which lie outside their boundaries, and these may sometimes have been omitted in the questionnaire returns or else counted twice. Another complication is that beds allocated for dementia sufferers may not be used for this purpose, while many beds not specifically allocated for this purpose are. The Health Advisory Services publication *The rising tide*[1] estimates (in 1981 figures) that about half the 38,500 patients in traditional psychiatric hospitals aged over 65 were suffering from age-related psychiatric disorders.

Although it is difficult or impossible to obtain detailed figures which are based on the same criteria, the general picture is clear.

TABLE 1: Specialist provision in England

NHS	Trad. Hosp.	Geriatric	DGH	Local Units	Total	%
	17,482	3,593	2,258	1,272	24,605	79
Local Auth.	Shires 2,169	Met. Boroughs 1,069	Lon. Bor. 751		3,989	12
Private	Nursing Homes 1,352	Resid. Homes 1,032	Vol. Resid. Homes 122		2,506	8
				GRAND TOTAL	31,100	

DGH—District General Hospital

TABLE 2: NHS Provision of specialist longstay care in England

Region	Psychiatric Trad hosp.	Geriatric	DGH	Local	Total
Northern	1799	192	277	136	2404
Yorkshire	1642	146	23	27	1838
Trent	1558	453	168	185	2364
East Anglia	1658	414	161	62	2295
N E Thames	957	573	181	173	1884
S E Thames	1651	201	132	79	2063
S W Thames	1112	105	51	97	1365
N W Thames	1255	80	430	39	1804
Wessex	857	44	18	82	1101
Oxford	391	117	—	44	552
S Western	1324	124	—	129	1577
W Midlands	1715	889	230	60	2894
Mersey	1163	193	158	—	1514
N Western	400	62	429	159	1050
Total	17482	3593	2258	1272	24705

In England at least 70 per cent of NHS longstay provision is still based in traditional psychiatric hospitals, while a mere 5 per cent is in the local units which are now officially recognised as the proper place for such provision. (Thirty-five such units were reported, with an average size of just over 30 beds.) Clearly there is a massive task ahead if the DHSS policy of phasing out isolated psychiatric hospitals, spelled out in a 1975 White Paper[2], is to be achieved and an even greater one if such patients are to be cared for in local 'homely' units rather than in hospital wards of any kind. Eleven years after the publication of this White Paper, very few traditional mental illness hospitals have closed their doors, in spite of government measures to encourage the use of NHS funds to pay for the care of hospitalised patients 'in the community', and the allocation of 16 million pounds between 1984 and 1987 to fund some pilot projects. Only five of these projects relate to provision for elderly mentally infirm people[3]. 'Active plans' are in hand to shut down 32 hospitals, but about 70 are likely to continue to provide a service in their own districts, and it is to be feared that, as the number of patients who have grown old in hospital decreases, their place will be taken by dementia sufferers for whom there is no alternative provision.

New initiatives in the NHS: Although very little has yet been achieved in terms of overall numbers or hospital closures, some interesting initiatives demonstrate the wide variety of ways in which the transfer of care from the longstay traditional hospitals may be carried out.

Two possible models, provided by Exeter and Central Manchester Health Authorities (HA) are described in detail on pages 174 and 184. A very different kind of answer is being planned in Lewisham HA where it is intended to provide up to twelve local NHS residential units, housing twelve patients each, over the next twelve years. Each unit, which is neutrally called a 'domus' (to differentiate it from nursing or residential care homes) will be built by a housing association, and residents will be able to claim constant attendance allowance and supplementary benefit with which to pay their rent. The staff will all be on a staff nurse grade, though they may not be trained as nurses, and they will work within a flat staff structure under an officer in charge who is responsible to NHS line management. Domestic and care roles will be blurred, and heavy emphasis will be placed on flexibility, privacy and choice in the way in which care is provided. These 'domuses' will be an integral part of the psychogeriatric service, providing all the longstay care in the district.

It is envisaged that three (preferably four) staff would need to be on duty during the day and two at night, giving a much higher staff/resident ratio than has been found anywhere in the course of preparing this study. The cost per resident is estimated at £19,000 per annum, £10,000 of which will be made available from the corresponding saving per patient made at Bexley Hospital; the rest will come from the residents' social security benefits to which, as tenants of a housing association, they will be entitled. Professor Elaine Murphy, who set up the project, was originally in favour of a still smaller unit of perhaps four residents, but became convinced that this would be too difficult to manage in terms of staffing, and that the death of a resident would leave too big a gap to be coped with.

A very different experiment is being undertaken by Dr Robin Philpott at Redcourt in Liverpool, where an NHS nursing home for the elderly mentally infirm is being set up on the same lines as the experimental nursing homes for the physically frail. A converted nurses' residence will take 23 longstay patients with severe dementia, who require substantial amounts of physical and psychiatric nursing care, from Rainhill Hospital. Administrative staffing has been modified so that a much larger percentage of revenue than usual is spent on direct patient care, and there is a ratio of 24 nurses and four patient-activity organisers to the 23 patients. The cost, at £16,000 per patient per annum, is about £3,000 more than the average for all Rainhill wards, including those catering for low dependency. The project will be closely monitored by the Institute of Human Ageing at Liverpool University in relation to costs as well as quality of care.

Both these projects seek to take patients out of a traditional hospital setting into a more 'domestic' environment, but it is of interest that a move in the reverse direction has also been tried with some success. Professor Tom Arie at the Department of Health Care of the Elderly, University of Nottingham Medical School, was provided with longstay beds for dementia sufferers at Coppice Hospital. This was a small, long-established psychiatric unit in beautiful grounds which, until the advent of the NHS, had been used by private patients and still had a 'graduate' population (psychotic patients who have grown old in hospital as opposed to new elderly patients) when the University psychogeriatric team took over.

The unit never worked well in its new role. The gardens were beautiful but difficult access meant that they were hardly used; transport problems hindered visiting and staff recruitment; upkeep was a constant headache; the building was unsuitable for heavy physical nursing; and the unit was cut off from the rest of the psychiatric division so that a constant threat of closure made good staff difficult to recruit and keep and funds hard to come by. Moreover the original staff and patients never really accepted the change of role. Eventually the Coppice Unit was closed and Professor Arie was offered two disused surgical wards in a tower block at the general hospital in the middle of Nottingham. Each of these provide three six-bedded wards, four single bedrooms, two day rooms and some smaller rooms with potential for small groups and activities. The setting could hardly be more clinical but the staff have added many domestic touches, and facilities for physical care are excellent. Large lifts make it relatively easy to take patients into the town centre which is on the hospital doorstep. The main gain, however, is seen as the improvement in staff morale. The new use for these wards helped to save the general hospital which was in danger of closure when the new University Hospital was opened, so the newcomers were welcomed (albeit with some trepidation about 'psychiatric patients'). The staff now feel part of a prestigious teaching unit with a weekly ward round run by the professor, and recruitment of well-qualified and motivated people is now easy.

Professor Arie says of the move in a personal communication to the author:

'Of course one wouldn't choose to plan a dementia unit in a tower block in a hospital in the centre of the city. But more and more I feel that the quality of care, given a basic adequacy of material environment to match the disabilities of the patients (rather than necessarily one that is ideal) depends mostly on adequate staff ratios (or the work becomes so impossible as to break everyone's spirit) and staff adequately trained and motivated and with a sense of being appreciated and supported. And there needs to be an adequate proportion of properly trained staff.

I could develop this a lot further, but what I get are many enquiries for advice on how such units should be *physically* planned; whereas I think human factors such as morale, motivation and training are much more important, and I am rarely asked about these. Fairly Heath Robinsonian solutions can often work when staffing is adequate, and they are happy.

It has been heartening that relatives of our patients, who were anxious about the move from the picturesque previous setting to the general hospital, without exception I think, are all now very pleased with the wards.'

Another possible approach is to transfer resources and primary responsibility for care from the NHS to a local authority. Thus the Hillingdon Health Authority and Social Services and Housing Departments are working out a joint approach to the care of elderly dependent people, providing forty people (who would otherwise have been admitted to residential care) with substantial extra support to enable them to remain at home, and using the vacancies to place forty hospitalised people suffering from severe dementia into small specialist wings in five residential homes. The HA is providing two community psychiatric nurses, along with occupational and physiotherapy staff to help support the people in these wings. The cost of adapting the homes concerned is being met by the SSD capital programme, but the extra level of staffing needed in the specialist wings (£30,000 per annum per home), the cost of providing the extra domiciliary care required (£60,000 per annum) and the cost of providing the NHS support staff (£41,000 per annum) is being met from a Care in the Community grant for the first three years. These costs will be picked up by the Local and Health Authorities at the end of three years, but the HA will save £13,000 per patient discharged and achieve one step towards the closure of St Bernard's Hospital, a traditional psychiatric hospital. The project is being monitored by the Personal Social Services Research Unit (PSSRU). Clearly, the goodwill of the local authority is paramount in carrying out a plan of this kind and Hillingdon is exceptional in its commitment to accepting responsibility for people who do not need constant medical and nursing care.

Although the Hillingdon project lays a lot of emphasis on multi-disciplinary co-operation, it does involve a transfer of responsibility to the local authority, but this is not necessarily the case. Thus Hastings HA and East Sussex SSD are working together to set up a specialist home combined with a 'community resource centre' and 'flexible day centre'. Admissions to the home will be controlled by the consultant psychiatrist working with members of a multi-disciplinary team, and the home will be run by nurses and care staff who will each be responsible to their own line management, though administrative responsibility will rest with the local authority. It is estimated that the new service will enable a longstay ward to be closed in Hellingley Hospital, saving over £300,000 a year, and Hastings HA is committing these funds to the project.

The initiatives described above involve the transfer of patients from traditional forms of care to some alternative which is thought to be preferable, but it will also be necessary and desirable to set up new forms of service to meet unmet needs. Thus the Wycombe HA, which is grossly under-provided with longstay beds, has gone into partnership with Buckinghamshire SSD to provide a 20-bed longstay, and assessment/shortstay facility in Highgrove House, a former GP maternity unit. No nursing staff are employed but there is sessional involvement from NHS occupational, speech and physiotherapists and a full-time CPN is attached to the unit. The consultant psychiatrist is in constant informal contact and all prospective residents will be known to, and have been assessed by, his Department of Mental Health of the Elderly (DMHE). Admission is decided by a multi-disciplinary assessment panel which comprises the OIC, the SSD principal homes officer, the social worker attached to the Unit, the CPN and the psychiatrist. Highgrove House is run with maximum emphasis on individual care and rehabilitation. It is unusual not only because of its regime and its 'partnership' base but also because of its role as a training resource, with a programme of seminars and conferences involving GPs, statutory and private residential care staff, and personnel from hospitals, sheltered housing and nursing homes. A seminar room has been built into the refurbished building.

Funding for this project, like Redcourt in Liverpool, was provided by the DHSS under its 'nursing home' budget (Special Medical Development) and by joint funding between the SSD and HA. Estimated total revenue cost is £260,000 per annum (£13,000 per resident) of which residents contributed £65,000 in 1985. The project is being monitored by Liverpool University.

These examples give some indication of the variety of means whereby the HAs are seeking to provide more domestic and localised care, but all these initiatives are a drop in the ocean of traditional hospital wards. A great deal of determination and commitment will be needed if the declared policy of closing traditional hospitals and providing longstay care within each district as an integral part of a psychogeriatric service, is to be achieved.

Local authority policy and provision
Shire counties: Only nine shire authorities (less than a quarter) do not have any specialist beds and most of these do in fact operate some kind of segregated provision within ordinary homes. Northamptonshire, Hertfordshire, Nottinghamshire, Staffordshire, Surrey and Dorset come into this category. Only two shire authorities—Cheshire and Derbyshire—make absolutely no claim to any sort of specialist provision.

The twenty English shire counties which do offer longstay specialist care are listed in Table 3 below in reverse order of the total number of beds provided.

It will be seen that there is a wide spectrum of provision, ranging from Cornwall, which has two longstay beds in a shortstay unit, to Hampshire with a total of 252 beds in six homes and two wings.

TABLE 3: Specialist longstay beds provided by shire counties

Authority	No of homes	No of Beds	No of Wings	No of beds	Total
Cornwall	2(1)	2	—	—	2
N Yorkshire	1	30	—	—	30
Durham	1	25	1(1)	10	35
Lincolnshire	1	38	—	—	38
Leicestershire	1	15	3	30	45
Buckinghamshire	1(1)	10	5	40	50
Cleveland	2(1)	46	1	12	58
Lancashire	1	31	3	30	61
Somerset	—	—	8	70	70
Devonshire	3(1)	72	—	—	72
Humberside	2	81	—	—	81
Suffolk	2	70	4	32	102
Bedfordshire	3	109	—	—	109
W Sussex	3(3)	110	—	—	110
Cambridgeshire	1	41	7(4)	71	112
Cumbria	4	108	1	10	118
E Sussex	4	140	1(1)	8	148
Essex	—	—	14	211	211
Kent	4(2)	140	2	83	223
Avon	8(1)	242	—	—	242
Hampshire	6	236	2	16	252
Total	50(10)	1546	52(6)	623	2169

Figures in brackets refer to joint funded provision.

Some authorities are of particular interest. Somerset, Essex and Cambridgeshire, for example, have opted wholeheartedly for the 'wing' solution although Cambridgeshire still has one 'traditional' specialist home. Buckinghamshire's provision is very small at present but it includes Highgrove House in High Wycombe which, as was noted above (page 15), is a pioneer example of health and social services collaboration funded by the DHSS. West Sussex has been particularly successful in obtaining joint funding and works in close association with the health authorities. It is a pioneer in the provision of purpose-built specialist homes based on the group-unit principle. East Sussex is experimenting with a jointly staffed residential and day care facility in Hastings (see page 15). However, the four largest providers amongst the shire counties, Kent, Essex, Avon and Hampshire, which between them offer a third of the longstay beds, give no detailed information about their service in their questionnaire responses.

Metropolitan districts: Of the 33 authorities which responded to the questionnaire (out of a possible 36), 12 said that they had no present or projected specialist care of any kind. These were Bolton, Barnsley, Wolverhampton, Wakefield, Tameside, Sunderland, South Tyneside, Salford, Oldham, North Tyneside, Manchester and Liverpool. However, some of these authorities are discussing improved services with the relevant health authority, or express fears that their homes will become '"specialist" by default'. Others with no present provision are considering some change. For example, Knowsley has hitherto pursued a policy of integration 'in the belief that the design of the buildings will accommodate this; that the size of the problem does not merit segregation; that the size of the Borough would raise the issue of stigma, problems of visiting and location; and in any event there would inevitably be the presence of some confused and difficult people in the homes anyway. Better staffing and greater acceptance of the care of confused people as a local authority responsibility has improved perception of this client group'. Nevertheless, Knowsley SSD is now considering some joint specialist provision with the HA. Rotherham had ambitious plans for a joint-funded 30 bed specialist home but this fell victim to cuts, and it is now considering a wing solution. A number of other authorities have very small-scale provision but over 80 per cent of the 1,069 beds provided by the metropolitan districts are to be found in only nine authorities and over half of these are in Stockport, Leeds and Newcastle. Details are given in Table 4:

TABLE 4: Specialist longstay beds provided by metropolitan districts

	No of Homes	Longstay beds	No of wings	Longstay beds
Wirral	1(1)	43	1	10
Bradford	3(2)	46	—	—
Sandwell	2	48	—	—
Trafford	2(2)	60	—	—
Sheffield	4	80	—	—
Dudley	2	77	—	—
Newcastle	5	179	—	—
Stockport	4	114	—	—
Leeds	6	222	—	—
Remainder (16 authorities)	5(3)	97	9(3)	93
Total	34(8)	966	10(3)	103
			TOTAL	1069

Joint funded units are shown in brackets.

It is interesting that the three largest providers say that they are not doing enough. Leeds is proposing to designate a further three homes as specialist provision, and Newcastle is considering the development of some additional specialist wings in its 'ordinary' homes, while Stockport state that 'because of the numbers of mentally infirm old people now in residential care, we feel that the *majority* of our elderly persons' homes which are already taking a high proportion of mentally infirm old people will need to be redesignated'. It is also of interest that at present only one of these 'high providers' also operates a specialist longstay wing.

London Boroughs: The London boroughs also show a very patchy pattern of provision with seven of the 33 authorities (22 per cent) providing 525 out of 751 beds (70 per cent). Of these the lions' share (342 beds) are in Croydon, Hillingdon and Newham. However, in contrast to the metropolitan districts, the London boroughs have invested heavily in the provision of specialist wings. Indeed, Hillingdon is using Care in the Community money to take 40 patients from St Bernard's Hospital into newly converted specialist wings (see page 14). Waltham Forest is of particular interest in that it runs a 35-bedded establishment called Francis House which is purpose-built on the group unit principle. One unit cares for people with chronic functional illness; one is for people suffering from 'a broad range of problems' including pre-senile dementia, personality disorders and changes in personality arising from stroke damage. The third provides for people with severe dementia presenting management problems. This kind of provision is unique as far as CPA is aware.

At the other end of the scale 15 of the 33 have no specialist provision at present but half of them (Sutton, Kensington and Chelsea, Islington, Hounslow, Hackney, Ealing, Brent and Camden) have thoughts, hopes or firm plans for some sort of specialist development in the near future, often in conjunction with a health authority. Thus, leaving aside the City of London (which has no homes) and Bromley (which is considering its policy) only Harrow, Haringey, Kingston, Lambeth and Richmond express no intention of making any provision in this field—an interestingly wide spectrum from the social point of view. Lambeth is unique in providing a carefully thought out statement on its 'integrationist' policy and the implications which this has for the way in which care must be provided in non-segregated settings.

Non-statutory sector
Private nursing homes: Private proprietors are as yet providing specialist care on a fairly limited scale. In the nursing home sector

TABLE 5: London boroughs providing specialist beds

	No of homes	No of Beds	No of Wings	No of Beds	
Tower Hamlets	1	32	1	8	40
Southwark	1	3(1)	2(1)	43	46
Barking & Dagenham	2	52	—	—	52
Westminster	—	—	4	45	45
Croydon	3	117	—	—	117
Newham	—	—	7	100	100
Hillingdon	1	30	8	95	125
Remainder providing less than 40 beds					
11 authorities	8(1)	117	8(1)	109	226
Total	16(1)	351	30(2)	400	751

Joint-funded provision in brackets

only 17 health authorities report any registrations at all and between them they total 42 homes providing 1,352 beds. As is to be expected, the greatest concentration is in the south coast (Brighton, Hastings, Eastbourne and Chichester HA's) but Croydon has registered three nursing homes providing 81 beds.

Only two authorities report nursing homes which 'specialise in practice' without being registered as such, but many respondents emphasise that all or many of the nursing homes in their area cater for some 'confused' patients. It is evident that the small number of 'specialist' beds enormously under-estimates the contribution which private nursing homes are making in this field, though probably they deal mainly with people who suffer from both physical and mental disability. Thus a detailed list of private provision compiled by the Age Concern Home Care Advisory Service in East Sussex shows that, although there are only two specialist nursing homes in the area covered, there are 37 which accept EMI patients[4].

Only 14 of the 42 homes are registered as mental nursing homes and it seems clear that authorities vary considerably in the extent to which they allow nursing homes without a specialist 'mental' registration to accept this kind of patient. Southport and Formby, at one extreme, keep a very close watch on the level of dementia being coped with in general nursing homes; and, while the registration officer would permit someone who developed dementia after admission to continue to be cared for if the home was managing adequately, she would not allow someone whose primary diagnosis was dementia to be admitted. By contrast, Wakefield HA says:-

'Nursing homes catering for the elderly may often accommodate people who are mentally confused, but this need not necessarily involve registration as a mental nursing home. In such cases the number of such patients and the seriousness of their condition needs to be carefully monitored by the person registered and the Wakefield Health Authority. It may be decided at some time that additional registration as a mental nursing home may be necessary.'[5]

Judging from the emphasis on the number of dementia sufferers in ordinary 'mixed' homes reported in many questionnaire returns, it is this latter approach (perhaps without the careful monitoring envisaged by Wakefield) which is followed by many registration authorities.

The higher level of fees payable from supplementary benefit to patients in any kind of nursing home care, compared with residential homes, appears to be encouraging a movement towards applications for nursing home registration, in spite of the accompanying requirement to have qualified nursing staff available at all times. Again, some authorities take much more trouble than others in agreeing guidelines with the local authority and ensuring that these are enforced. Southport and Formby, which offers an outstanding example of good practice in this respect, says in relation to the role of mentally registered nursing homes:-

'The Health Authority recognises the broad span of care required for mentally ill patients from a residential care home or rest home on the one hand, through nursing homes to hospital care on the other. Most physically well but mentally ill patients will be managed in rest homes or residential care homes with the help of the community psychiatric services. More severely mentally ill patients with behaviour problems such as aggressive behaviour may well need to be managed in hospital. There is, however, a growing need for nursing homes which will accept mentally disordered patients who are also physically ill and requiring nursing care for this illness. Mentally registered nursing homes will, therefore, care for mentally disturbed or disordered patients who in addition need nursing care for their physical illnesses. The authority will need to be convinced of the need for registration of homes caring for those patients who are not physically ill.'[6]

A joint report was written by Southport and Formby HA and Sefton SSD after visiting all the specialist private provision in the area. This emphasises the need for qualified psychogeriatric assessment of suitability for a particular form of care and remarks on the 'danger' that RMN-trained nurses running residential homes will attract people who require nursing care. It concludes that 'the vast majority of homes should have a dual registration' and that all six specialist residential homes 'had in our opinion residents who needed psychiatric nursing'.[7]

Private residential homes: Specialist care in the residential sector is also found mainly in the shire counties. Twenty counties reported a total of 49 specialist homes providing 827 beds and 66 homes providing 1,149 beds which the registration officer considered were 'SIP' though they were not formally registered as such. The latter figure is, however, distorted by Kent where either the practice is exceptionally common or the registration officer's standards are unusually strict, for Kent claimed 13 'SIP' homes providing 364 beds. Details of provision in authorities with more than 50 such beds in the combined categories are given in Table 6. It will be seen that yet again East Sussex dominates the scene with 232 beds in specialist homes, over 100 more than Cornwall its nearest rival. Provision of this kind in the metropolitan boroughs is minimal with the notable exception of Sefton which, perhaps because of its highly developed registration system and close co-operation with the DHA, reports seven homes providing 141 beds. The London boroughs have only one specialist home in Bromley, but they report nine homes providing 121 beds which specialise in practice. The private residential sector's registered contribution is therefore mainly limited to a small number of shire counties, though again the point must be made that many non-specialist homes do care for dementia sufferers. The Age Concern Home Advisory Service in East Sussex, quoted above, lists 441 non-specialist residential care homes of which 114 state their willingness to accept EMI residents[8].

The private sector is not only patchy in geographical terms but also varied in quality. Thus one registration officer who has two homes in his area recommends one of them strongly but says of the other: 'It has recently changed ownership; the former proprietor resorted to providing for the EMI through failure to attract mentally alert residents. There are no specialist facilities in the home and both the present and previous proprietors have made unsuccessful attempts to revert to a non-EMI group'. It is this type of 'specialist' provision in the private sector which needs to be constantly guarded against.

Voluntary provision: The specialist contribution of the voluntary sector in England is very limited. CPA has been unable to identify any voluntary nursing homes. In the residential sector three organisations, Hill Homes, the Jewish Welfare Board and Servite Houses, provide a total of 74 beds in the London area and there are one 20-bedded home in Hertfordshire and three in Cornwall which between them provide 20 beds, making a grand total of 122. Age Concern Southwark is planning a new-build specialist

TABLE 6: Specialist private residential care

	Spec. Homes	Beds	'SIP'	Beds	Total
Shire counties:					
Devon	2	37	1	23	60
Lincoln	—	—	2	73	73
Cambs	1	8	3	67	75
Essex	5	54	8	103	157
Hants	4	38	14	155	193
Cornwall	14	145	3	65	210
Kent	—	—	13	364	364
E Sussex	10	232	7	178	410
Remainder					
(12 authorities)	13	312	15	121	433
Total	49	826	66	1,149	1,976
Metropolitan Boroughs					
Sefton	7	141	—	—	141
Remainder					
(5 authorities)	3	30	3	23	53
Total	10	171	3	23	194
London Boroughs					
(8 authorities)	1	34	9	121	155
Total England	60	1,031	78	1,293	2.324

home for 30 people under the Care in the Community programme. A few authorities report some specialisation in practice, particularly by large institutions run by religious orders, such as the Sisters of Nazareth and The Little Sisters of the Poor, but from the information available it does not seem that the percentage of dementia sufferers cared for in these homes is much higher than in many local authority homes. It seems a pity that the voluntary sector is not doing more to provide some models of good care in this field, especially as the Church of Scotland's Williamwood House has shown (see page 242) it can do so with great success.

Wales
Welsh Office initiatives

Unlike Northern Ireland, Wales does not have a relatively homogeneous approach to the way in which specialist dementia services should be provided, nor does it have a uniform concentration of provision in traditional hospital care, as is found in Scotland. Its nine health authorities and eight local authorities vary in character from the concentrated and urban to the vast and rural, and they are equally varied in levels of provision and ways in which they are tackling the task. However, they have in the Welsh Office a Department which is unique in the United Kingdom, in that it acts as a regional health authority and is also responsible for policy relating to housing, health, social services, medical services, nursing and education. All these policy divisions work under the same roof and are responsible to the same Secretary of State. They are thus free from the barriers which are built into the segregated departments of government in England; they do not have the tension of including the social security sector within the structure, and they are dealing with a small group of authorities whose staff can be known and consulted on an individual basis—albeit across horrendous geographical barriers. Potentially, therefore, the Welsh Office is in a relatively good position to shape policy, though the lack of resources and small size of its staff make it impossible to focus on all issues simultaneously and it tends to deal with one policy issue and then turn to the next. The first major exercise of this kind has been in the field of mental handicap where there is a clearly established national strategy. Lessons about methods of planning at central and local level and the importance of having a financial reward to offer are now being applied to other fields, including the care of the elderly.

The Department has published a policy document *Policies and priorities for health services in Wales*[9] which states that health authorities should devote *additonal* resources annually (equivalent to at least 0.5 per cent of their total budgets) to the development of 'community and continuing care services for mentally handicapped and elderly people and those suffering from mental illness'. The funds for this expansion are to be secured from efficiency savings 'which do not involve any reduction in either the volume or quality of existing services'. The paper also advocates the development of a network of 'smaller local and community hospitals' around the district general hospitals (DGHs) which will treat patients who do not require DGH facilities, including 'geriatric facilities and services for people with dementia'. The next stage will be the publication of a corporate plan for the NHS in Wales which will set more detailed objectives and targets, including plans for the longstay sector. The HAs will then be asked to start on a new cycle of strategic planning which is consistent with regional policy and which has a strong emphasis on multi-disciplinary service provision, community care and inter-authority co-operation. Inevitably it will be a long time before these measures bear fruit. A recent discussion document *A good old age: An initiative on the care of the elderly in Wales*[10] though admirable in its sentiments, 'advocates virtue' rather blandly and does not set out to address the needs of particular groups, including dementia sufferers, in detail. However it has produced quite a lively discussion and some constructive responses.

Present provision
As Table 7 shows, almost all the specialist provision which does exist is in traditional geriatric or mental illness hospitals. However, Gwent and South Glamorgan health and local authorities have made a start on achieving change by producing joint strategy documents. The former covers services for the mentally ill of all age groups, and the changes proposed in relation to the elderly are mainly in terms of better day hospital and assessment facilities; nothing is said about the local authority contribution in providing specialist care[11]. The South Glamorgan document however is specifically on psychogeriatric services by a joint multi-disciplinary working party and it is a detailed and hard-hitting piece of work. It goes into considerable detail about the 'inadequacy of the resources provided, the inappropriate way in which they are used and the totally haphazard way in which the needs of patients/residents are met.' It considers local authority homes to be grossly understaffed in relation to the dependency of the residents. (This point had already been forcefully made in a report by the Director of Social Services, which was attached to the report as an appendix.) It recommends a major improvement in the staffing of ordinary homes and the establishment of a number of specialist homes with twice the existing staffing norms and 'approaching the levels existing in a psychogeriatric ward'[12]. However, it appears from the questionnaire returns that so far the only solid result of these recommendations is a joint-funded, 20 place unit providing 12 assessment and eight longstay beds which is due to open in 1986. Gwynedd, which until recently had no specialist beds of its own at all, has

TABLE 7: Specialist provision in Wales

NHS	Trad	Geriatric	DGH	Local	TOTAL
Gwent	264	—	74	—	338
Gwynedd	—	—	—	24	24
East Dyfed	153	29	—	—	182
S Glamorgan	139	38	—	—	177
W Glamorgan	—	369	—	58	427
Total	556	436	74	82	1,148

(Clwyd, Powys, Pembrokeshire and Mid-Glamorgan have no specialist beds at present.)

Local authority provision

	No of Homes	No of Beds	No of Wings	No of Beds	Total
Clwyd	1	24	1(1)	9	33
Dyfed	2	80	1	15	95
Gwent	—	—	3(3)	41	41
S Glamorgan	—	—	—	—	—
Mid Glamorgan	3	116	—	—	116
W Glamorgan	1	38	1	6	44
Total	7	258	6(4)	71	329

(Figures in brackets refer to provision joint funded.)
Gwynedd and Powys have no specialist beds at present.

Private sector provision
(nursing homes)

	No of Homes	No of Beds
Clwyd	2(2)	70
Gwent	2(2)	77
Gwynedd	1(1)	18
Total	5(5)	185

(Figures in brackets indicate the number registered as a mental nursing home.)

Residential Homes

	No of Homes	No of Beds
W Glamorgan	1	5
Clwyd	2	30
Total	3	35

now commissioned a 24-bed unit for the continuing care of psychogeriatric patients within the grounds of a local hospital for the mentally handicapped, which will take back patients currently being cared for by an adjacent health authority. Within the next five years between six and eight assessment beds and approximately 50 longstay beds will also be provided, but the main focus is the development of community services and 'informal nursing day care units'. Since Gwynedd covers 1,500 square miles, any form of service development inevitably faces formidable logistical problems. The District has as yet no psycho-geriatrician. Mid Glamorgan has 411 longstay psychogeriatric beds but does not distinguish between functional and organic illness. It is making a detailed 'census' of dementia sufferers known to the HA as a basis for long-term planning. East Dyfed, which has not yet produced any policy statement in this field, has provided one 29-bedded psychogeriatric unit in the grounds of a geriatric hospital and is also using joint funding to bring the empty wing of a Part III home into use and staff it with 2.5 wte RMNs and four additional care assistants to provide 12 additional EMI places. Pembrokeshire has no longstay provision of its own and Powys has no policy statement and no separate psychogeriatric service. All elderly people are cared for by generalist psychiatrists with no separately allocated resources.

There is therefore a very long way to go in the Welsh HAs, and the same is true of the LAs. The South Glamorgan report quoted above is not likely to represent an exceptional situation in terms of either unmet need or inadequate staffing. Mid Glamorgan provides three specialist homes and has produced a report summarising *The rising tide*[13] and its implications for both carers and the SSD. However, it is not proposing to increase its longstay sector any further and is concentrating on the provision on relief beds and flexible day care. Dyfed with two homes and a wing also has relatively extensive provision. In addition to the South Glamorgan joint-funded unit noted above it is planning to develop specialist groups within its Part III homes. Clwyd has one specialist home and one wing, both joint-funded, and is proud of the quality of care offered in the latter. It too is moving towards specialist wings and a jointly-financed community support team. Powys is planning to provide at least 40 beds in specialist wings though none is in operation at present and Gwent already has three such wings with higher staffing ratios, specialist training programmes and multi-disciplinary assessment/review procedures. Things are therefore beginning to move, but, as elsewhere in the UK, there is an immensely long way to go.

Given the overall level of provision, the private sector is relatively well represented on the north Welsh 'costa geriatrica'. There are five specialist mental nursing homes providing 165 beds which cater for elderly people, though these may include mixed-age nursing homes taking people discharged from longstay psychiatric hospitals.

Specialist residential care offers only two homes in Clwyd and one in West Glamorgan, providing 35 beds in all, while a further two homes (55 beds) in Clwyd are said to specialise in practice.

Scotland
Present provision
Specialist care in Scotland is provided almost entirely in traditional psychiatric hospitals, and the way in which it is given often makes no clear distinction between functional and organic illness. Like the data obtained from other parts of the UK, therefore, the figures may not be very accurate but they do show very clearly the overall pattern of specialist care.

TABLE 8: Specialist provision for dementia sufferers in Scotland

	Trad	Geriatric	DGH	Local	Total
Argyll & Clyde	376	—	—	—	376
Ayrshire & Arran	342	—	—	—	342
Borders	187	—	—	—	187
Dumfries & Galloway	204	—	—	—	204
Fife	322	—	180	—	502
Forth Valley	360	—	—	—	360
Grampion	524	—	—	30	554
*Greater Glasgow	1050	—	—	—	1050
Lothian	843	24	—	36	903
Tayside	552	24	24	26	626
Total	4760	48	204	92	5104

*The Greater Glasgow figure is given as 'between 1000 and 1100'. The total has not been broken down between different types of hospital.

(Highland, Forth Valley, Shetland, Orkney, Western Isles and Lanarkshire have no allocated longstay psychogeriatric beds but Highland Forth Valley and Lanarkshire have large mental illness hospitals.)

Local authority provision is currently limited to one eight-bedded 'wing' in the Borders where it is planned to build six more specialist wings providing 48 beds in six new homes during the next five years. There was no private specialist provision at the time of writing.

As elsewhere in the UK, ordinary local authority homes house a high proportion of elderly people with mental disability, as do the homes run by the voluntary sector (which provides a substantial number of the residential places in Scotland). But for the most part they do not see such care as their proper task, and so, with the recent and notable exception of Williamwood House, a pioneer specialist home provided by the Church of Scotland (see page 242) responsibility in this field has remained with the NHS.

Policy recommendations
This concentration on traditional hospital care has been challenged a number of times. As early as 1961 a government report said that 'The object of every local authority must be to expand their mental health services of all age groups to the point at which *no person need be resident in hospital unless he will benefit from or requires hospital care*'[14]. Ten years later the hard hitting and far sighted Millar Report, produced by a sub-committee of the Standing Medical Advisory Committee[15], said that they had been deeply impressed by a visit to a pioneer specialist home called 'The Green' at Redruth in Cornwall where:-

'Many of the residents had quite marked degrees of mental abnormality. One third of them were occasionally incontinent and a further third required some assistance with dressing. Two thirds were on medication given out by the matron or her assistant. The problem of wandering had been overcome to some extent by the ground floor being designed on the open plan system with numerous window bays where the patients could sit in comfort. The general practitioner handled the day-to-day medical care of the patients. There was close contact with an associated psychogeriatric unit, and generally it was the policy that no patient was admitted without first having been assessed in the psychogeriatric unit. No member of the staff had any formal nurse training.

Under present conditions patients such as these are placed in mental hospitals when in fact a special home for the elderly confused would be more appropriate. We believe that there are many advantages in homes of this type as compared with hospital type accommodation. Such homes developed to date are relatively small with 30–50 places, and therefore it is possible to build them in locations which do not physically separate the residents from their former home environment or their relatives and friends. In this way the community ties with the home become very strong.'

The committee went on to suggest that as local authorities were likely to be reluctant on financial grounds to take over what had traditionally been an NHS responsibility, there was a case for central government making capital and revenue grants to local authorities to provide specialist care. Alternatively some joint financial arrangement might be made between hospitals and local authorities. 'Early guidance should be given by central government so that these homes are included in the development plans for the immediate years ahead.'[16]

Unfortunately no action was taken on these recommendations, and eight years later yet another committee produced 'The Timbury Report' also on services for the elderly with mental disability[17]. This specifically disagreed with the Millar Report's view of specialist provision though it gave no reasons for doing so. It stated:

'3.3 At present, local authorities accommodate in residential homes for the elderly a proportion of residents with mental disability. In most cases the residents have become mentally disabled after admission but some have been mildly mentally disabled at the time of admission. Where a resident becomes severely disabled it has been possible to arrange transfer to a mental illness hospital, but with the increasing numbers of elderly persons aged 75 and over this is becoming more difficult.

In our view, the present arrangements whereby local authorities admit elderly persons to residential accommodation, mainly for social reasons, are perfectly acceptable and should continue. Local authorities, however, should not be expected to admit to residential accommodation persons who have a mental disability, as diagnosed by a psychiatrist, which will have an unsettling effect on other residents. Nor should they be expected to continue to provide accommodation for persons who, while in residence, become mentally disabled to the point where their continued residence would have an upsetting effect on other residents and the general day-to-day functioning of the home. Those who should not be admitted to residential accommodation in the first instance, and also those who should be transferred to some other form of accommodation because of mental disability, are more properly the responsibility of the health service, which would of course require additional resources to meet this need.

3.4 Unlike the 'Millar' Committee we do not consider that local authorities should be expected to provide separate residential homes for the elderly with mental disability. As noted in the previous paragraph we accept that some residents of homes for the elderly become mentally disabled after admission and we would see such persons continuing in residence until such time as the level of their mental disability required that they be transferred to health service accommodation.'[16]

The Timbury report did, however, recognise that psychiatric hospital wards were not the answer and the committee went on to advocate a massive building programme of relatively small and local continuing care units in single storey buildings containing 40 or 60 beds in three groups of 20. They envisaged that each unit should contain four single rooms and four four-bedded rooms. 'The dining and sitting areas, which should be separate, should not be required to accommodate more than 24 patients (allowing for three or four day patients) and should be domestic in design and furnishing'. The Report recommended that the Scottish Office should take immediate steps to produce an appropriate building note for these units.

With hindsight it seems perhaps fortunate that no action was taken. A building note for these mini-hospital units was never produced, and none were built though there are five units in the country, which are said to offer 'Timbury style care'. In 1980, two years after the Timbury Report was published, the Scottish Health Authorities Priorities for the Eighties (SHAPE) report[17] again acknowledged that a great many elderly people with dementia were inappropriately placed in large mental and general hospitals[18], and a Home and Health Department Circular drew attention to the importance of joint planning[19]. It also set out a scheme for support financing of local authority provision by health boards. Five years after that, in 1985, a Scottish Office Circular emphasised yet again the urgent need to provide alternatives, though in comfortably vague terms[20]. It said:-

'It is generally accepted that a significant proportion of long-stay hospital patients would be more appropriately cared for by other forms of NHS provision, for example, continuing care units; or in hostels, group homes and other residential facilities provided by local authorities and voluntary organisations; or with suitable support in their own homes (which might be special needs accommodation provided by local authorities or housing associations). At the same time, there are people being cared for in local authority accommodation, or in their own homes, whose emerging needs would be more appropriately met by the NHS. The Secretary of State believes that there is a need to develop more flexible patterns of care, emphasising the expansion of non-institutional services within the community, as a means of improving the quality for those concerned.'[20]

In spite of the reference above to local authorities, the Scottish Home and Health Department appears to take the view that the NHS should provide for the care of dementia sufferers, and that a proportion of this care should be in continuing care units, but it is currently reconsidering its views on the size and design of the units. It is, however, hard to imagine where the funds for new building on the scale required will be found, although some of the health boards are considering, or have already committed themselves to, a policy of localisation.

Scottish Action on Dementia
All in all, therefore, it is not surprising that speaking at a meeting called in 1985 to launch a new campaign 'Scottish Action on Dementia' (SAD) Dr W Boyd, a leading consultant psychogeriatrician, said:-

'... I have to emphasise to you that over the last decade I have watched my colleagues attempting to provide services for the elderly with dementia and I have seen their enthusiasm give way to anger and their anger to frustration and their frustration to a sense of utter hopelessness.'[21]

SAD, a coalition of concerned organisations, is sponsored by the Mental Health Foundation and Age Concern Scotland, and it seeks to generate national and local improvement of service provision through various forms of pressure group activity. Its policies are based on a detailed analysis of priorities and strategies for change[22]. In the field of longstay care it supports the Timbury Report's advocacy of small local continuing care units, although it emphasises the need for such units to be accessible, fully integrated with other community-based services, able to offer day care, respite care and support for informal carers as well as longstay beds, and served by professionals with a wide range of skills.

It says that 'unlike Timbury' it advocates a 'flexible approach' as to how such units should be funded and staffed (whether they should be an NHS or local authority responsibility) and it diplomatically does not commit itself on the contentious issue of who should control admission or how far it will still be necessary to provide beds in psychiatric hospitals for severely disturbed elderly dementia sufferers.

There is no doubt, however, that Scottish Action on Dementia has a long and uphill task ahead. A great deal of effort and a heavy pressure of informed public opinion will be needed to change Scotland's traditional methods of care provision and ensure not only that localised continuing care units and other community-based services are provided, but also that they are given the resources, the staff, the training and access to professional expertise to do their job properly.

Northern Ireland
A planned 'continuum of care'
In some respects Northern Ireland is ahead of the rest of the UK in the construction of a planned service for dementia sufferers, although there is a very long way to go before the plan (which is already in operation in South Belfast) becomes a reality throughout the Province. Progress will be facilitated by the joint responsibility for both health and social services carried by the four health and social services boards, and by a well-established tradition of providing specialist care in the social services

departments which goes back to a pilot scheme at Ferrard House in Antrim (see page 143 for a detailed description).

The model which was established in South Belfast by Dr J N Scott and Mr R Ferguson (Assistant Director of Social Services) is based on the concept of a continuum of care, ranging from various home support services for the majority, through appropriate residential care for intermediate groups—including a day hospital and a 30-bedded specialist home (Orchardville)—and on to hospital nursing care for those considered to require it. There is active involvement at all levels of need with the local geriatric service and very strong emphasis on close collaboration between the specialist psychiatrist and the social services; a collaboration which is all the more necessary because of the high proportion of elderly people in the population of the district (17 per cent compared with 14 per cent in the whole of Belfast and 11.1 per cent outside Belfast). South Belfast is also one of the poorest-resourced districts in Northern Ireland in terms of ordinary residential home provision—40 per cent below target with a shortfall of 350 places.

Orchardville was set up in 1981 in close co-operation with Dr Scott who sees and assesses all referrals with social work colleagues and attends a case review at the home every three or four months. At this meeting the officer in charge (OIC) of the home, the psychiatrist, trainee registrars, and the senior social worker in line management of Orchardville, review all present residents, consider the transfer of those thought to require some other form of care, discuss the waiting list and agree on priorities. Thus, although Orchardville is clearly understood to be a social service facility, since the inception of the service model in 1981 all decisions about suitability and admission priority have been agreed by the core team members. The hospital facilities under Dr Scott's control comprise 36 mixed-sex longstay beds for dementia sufferers (functional illness is treated in the nearby general hospital psychiatric unit); a 24-bedded shortstay unit for relief admission, assessment and patients awaiting transfer; and a day hospital for dementia sufferers. A service based on the same concept of a 'continuum of care' is now being developed in the two other Belfast health care districts. One specialist home is already functioning and another is due to open shortly. Outside Belfast there are specialist homes in Antrim, Craigavon, Lisburn, Monkstown, and Londonderry providing a total of 241 beds in the Province, although not all the homes have psychogeriatric and geriatric links which are as explicit as in Orchardville.

The 'continuum of care' model assumes that while some residents will be cared for until death others will deteriorate physically or behaviourally to a level which significantly affects the quality of life of other residents and also changes their own care needs so that they really require full-time geriatric or psychogeriatric nursing care. Thus, since Orchardville opened, 10 residents have died within the home, 11 have been transferred to a geriatric hospital, 24 to a psychogeriatric hospital and three have been rehabilitated sufficiently for transfer to ordinary residential care.

Apart from the wards in Purdyburn Hospital referred to above, provision in the six traditional psychiatric hospitals does not yet differentiate very clearly between 'graduates,' dementia sufferers and elderly people with recent functional illness, so outside Belfast the hospital end of the 'continuum of care' is still very under-developed. However, Dr Scott has his base in a department of Belfast City Hospital which is also the clinical unit of the Department of Mental Health in the Queen's University of Belfast. All the psychiatrists trained in this department have at least six month's experience working under Dr Scott in psycho-geriatrics, so there are trained doctors accustomed to the South Belfast model available to fill the specialist posts now provided in each of the health boards. A considerable improvement in the quality of psychogeriatric care can therefore be expected soon and this will be combined with a reduction in the number of psychiatric hospital beds. It is hoped to cut these by 20 per cent by 1992 and a large proportion of those closed will be in the longstay/elderly category. It is proposed that resources released by this will be transferred to community-based services, including specialist residential care and other social services provision—a transfer which the joint system of provision in Northern Ireland makes easier than elsewhere in the UK. As in Scotland, specialist provision in the non-statutory sector is as yet virtually non-existent although 'ordinary' private nursing homes and residential homes are beginning to mushroom.

Conclusion
This brief and sketchy attempt to show the general situation with regard to specialist care in the United Kingdom shows much local variation, but there are a number of conclusions which are common to the whole of the country.

1. However hard we work to provide local and 'homely' units of care, a great many people are going to be looked after in traditional hospital wards of one kind or another for a long time to come. It is therefore not enough to stress the desirability of closing traditional hospitals, important though that is as a long-term goal. We must *also* make every effort to achieve the kind of good practice illustrated in this report *within* traditional hospital settings. This can be done, provided they can be upgraded to offer what Professor Arie calls 'a basic adequacy of material environment' (page 14). Given this basic adequacy, the crucial factor in the provision of good care is not the building but the level of staffing and the training, motivation and support which the staff are offered.

2. Communication and co-operation between health and social services are still at an abysmally low level. Only 16 examples of joint-funded specialist provision were found and only one example of genuinely fused service provision (see page 15). We can only provide adequately for people with severe dementia when this artificial gap is bridged and it is recognised in both practice and theory that we need trained residential social care workers in NHS settings, and we need people with psychology, nursing, OT, physiotherapy, and speech therapy skills working in the local authority and private sectors.

3. Over 7,000 people are already being provided for in localised specialist units of one kind or another, but localised care is not necessarily good care; it may be both out of sight and out of mind and subject to all the possible malpractices with none of the compensatory safeguards of care in traditional hospitals. *Wherever* care is provided, the authorities concerned, whether as providers or as inspectors have a duty to measure it against the standards which are set out in *Home life: A code of practice for residential care*[22] and promote the quality of care which this report shows is possible.

REFERENCES

1. *The rising tide: developing services for mental illness in old age*. National Health Service, Health Advisory Service, Sutton, 1982.

2. Department of Health and Social Security, *Better services for the mentally ill*. HMSO, London, 1975.

3. *Care in the community: descriptions of projects for elderly people*. Discussion Paper No 406, PSSRU, University of Kent at Canterbury, 1985.

4. *Registered residential care and nursing homes in East Sussex*. Age Concern East Sussex, Home Care Advisory Service, Lewes, 1985.

38

5. *Guidelines for the inspection and registration of private nursing homes.* Wakefield Health Authority, 1985.

6. *Notes of guidance on the registration and the conduct of nursing homes.* Southport and Formby and South Sefton District Health Authorities, Southport, 1985.

7. G H Murray, A Phillips and C Waldson, *Report on mentally registered residential care homes and nursing homes in Sefton.* Sefton SSD 1985 (unpublished).

8. Age Concern East Sussex, op. cit.

9. *Policies and priorities for health services in Wales.* Welsh Office, Cardiff, 1985.

10. *A good old age: an initiative on the care of the elderly in Wales.* Welsh Office, Cardiff, 1985.

11. *Joint strategy for the mentally ill.* Gwent Health Authority and Gwent County Council, 1983.

12. South Glamorgan Health Authority (Teaching) and County of South Glamorgan Social Services Committee Working Party to review mental illness services in, *South Glamorgan Report No 1 Psychogeriatric services 1984.*

13. *The rising tide*, op. cit.

14. Scottish Health Services Council Standing Advisory Committee on Local Authority Services, *Mental health services of local health authorities.* HMSO, Edinburgh, 1961.

15. Scottish Home and Health Department, *Services for the elderly with mental disorder.* HMSO, Edinburgh, 1970.

16. Ibid.

17. Scottish Health Service Planning Council and Advisory Council on Social Work, *Services for the elderly with mental disability in Scotland.* HMSO, Edinburgh, 1979.

18. Scottish Home and Health Department, *Scottish health authorities priorities for the eighties.* (SHAPE report). HMSO, Edinburgh, 1980.

19. *Joint planning and support financing arrangements.* Scottish Home and Health Department, Edinburgh, 1980. (Circular 1980 (GEN) 5, 14 March.)

20. *Community care joint planning and support finance.* Scottish Home and Health Department, Edinburgh, 1985. (NHS circular 1985 (GEN) 18, 24 April.)

21. Age Concern Scotland, *Scottish Action on Dementia: campaigning for better services for dementia sufferers and their carers in Scotland.* Scottish Action on Dementia, Edinburgh, 1985.

22. J Killeen, *Dementia in Scotland: priorities for care, strategies for change.* Scottish Action on Dementia, Edinburgh, 1986.

23. *Home life: a code of practice for residential care.* Centre for Policy on Ageing, London, 1984.

3 Analysis of findings from the case studies

Selection and methodology

The selection of specialist establishments for the 14 case studies which are the heart of this project was necessarily arbitrary. The DHSS criteria were that they should be independent units of not more than 30 beds, provide high-quality care, be geographically dispersed and include provision from health, social services and the private sector. These guidelines have been followed in the main, but it seemed desirable to include one ward in a traditional psychiatric hospital and one ward within a specialist ESMI unit set in a district general hospital as a point of comparison with the kind of care offered in more domestic surroundings.

Suggestions for inclusion in the study were initially obtained from members of the Royal College of Psychiatry who have a special interest in this field. Recommendations were also sought from local authority specialists in residential care and other CPA contacts, and the list was completed from responses to questionnaires sent to all health authorities and social services departments (see chapter 2). The staff of all the establishments included make a real effort to provide a high quality of care, but because of the very diffferent levels of physical and mental disability in the client group they are catering for; and the wide range of resources available in terms of building, furniture and staff levels, the outcome inevitably varies considerably. No attempt has been made, therefore, to put them in any kind of 'rank order' and comments on the way in which care is provided have been kept as neutral as possible, though personal predilections are inevitably reflected in the way in which the material is presented.

It should be noted that each case study describes the establishment concerned *at the time of the visit* and in some cases considerable changes have been made since then.

The material in the case studies was obtained by visiting each establishment at different times over 24 hours, including late evening and early morning: observing what was going on; looking at records; talking to the staff on duty, the residents and their relatives; and obtaining any written material relating to 'philosophy', assessment procedures, staff training etc, which was available. A detailed checklist was used to assist this process (see

Appendix I). Every visit included a long discussion with the person in charge of the unit, during which he or she was asked to complete a rating scale for each resident using the Crichton Royal Behavioural Rating Scale (CRBRS) relating to 'memory', 'orientation' and 'communication'. This scale (which is described on page 45) has been found to correlate well with clinical assessments of dementia and has enabled a rough and ready estimate to be made both of the average level and the range of disability with which each home is coping. (A zero score indicates complete lucidity and a score of 11, total lack of ability in all three areas.) It was not practicable in the time available to make any detailed assessment of physical disability, but general observations are included in the report. The person in charge was also asked about the professional support services used by the establishment. These service providers were then asked for their views on the quality of care provided, the level of disability the home could cope with, the amount of work it generated and its relevance to the provision of psychogeriatric services in the area.

Detailed accounts of the establishments included in the report are provided on pages 93–254 with particular emphasis on the unique approach of each one. The present section takes the same material and analyses it in comparative terms, seeking to draw out the significance of variations in practice and highlight aspects of provision which seem to be of particular interest or value. It looks at the range of disability catered for and the advantages and disadvantages of various types of building and design and then goes on to consider the ways in which care givers can promote or detract from residents' individuality, right to choose, right to be active and dignity of image. This is followed by a discussion of staff levels, training and communication and various methods of assessment, and the chapter concludes with some brief comments on the availability of generalist and specialist professional support in the areas concerned.

Brief description of selected establishments
To assist the reader to make sense of this analysis before referring to the detailed studies, the salient characteristics of each unit are described below. The order is necessarily arbitrary and does not imply any judgement on the quality of service provided.

Social services provision
Bemerton Lodge, Special Unit, Salisbury—a ten-place special care unit, is a purpose-built extension to what was originally a 50-place

residential home with a large attached day centre facility. The design is unusual in that it provides a large central space, lit principally by a skylight, for all social activity and this is surrounded by single bedrooms, bathroom and lavatory accommodation, a kitchenette and access to an enclosed garden. Internal passages have thus been eliminated and ample space for movement and activity is combined with free access to personal rooms and easy supervision. The unit currently also provides four day care places each weekday and consideration is being given to using one longstay place for relief and respite care. The regime lays strong emphasis on continuous gentle reality-orientation in one-to-one conversation, group activity graded according to ability, and involvement in customary domestic activity and self care. Residents have severely impaired short-term memory and have proved unsuitable for non-segregated care, but retain a good deal of capacity for communication and self care.

Flat Two, Orchard House, Cambridge—is an eight-bedded unit in a local authority home built on the group unit principle. It provides specialist care for people with a severe level of both physical and mental disability with a strong emphasis on 'key worker' responsibility, one-to-one contact and a 'problem-solving' approach to difficulties. Staff levels are low but the quality of training and support is high. As such, it is of particular interest as an example of the 'wing solution' to providing specialised care without any drastic adaptation of premises. Other features of interest are the use of 'personal history books' to bring the past experience of residents to life for them and for the staff, the regular involvement of a psychologist in staff support and training, and a detailed method of 'care planning'.

Bole Hill View, Sheffield—is a purpose-built local authority specialist home which combines 25 longstay beds, five shortstay and respite/emergency places and a 20-place day centre with the objective of offering a continuum of support throughout the period of dependency. The 'philosophy' is strongly oriented towards individualised care using distraction and collusion rather than confrontation in the management of difficult or deluded behaviour and with a high tolerance of 'calculated risk'. However, severe constraints are imposed on the regime by the design of the building and the combination of different forms of care in a relatively large institution.

Vernon House, Stockport—is a long-established home providing specialist care for 30 (now reduced to 28) very severely disabled people (including one shortstay bed). It has the lowest staffing level found in this report. A new unit providing for six shortstay residents has recently been added as a Demonstration Development District (DDD) project. The quality of care offered, though good when related to the building, levels of dependency, and levels of staffing, is not remarkable, but the home has been included in the study because it offers interesting points of comparison with Bole Hill View; because a number of issues are raised by the addition of the DDD project; and because it operates in a health district where there is an ESMI unit but no psychogeriatrician. Stockport's plans for training care staff are also of considerable interest. The home demonstrates very clearly that specialist SSD care must always be considered in the context of other service provision.

Ferrard House, Antrim—is an attractive purpose-built single storey home opened in 1970 which provides 31 beds, mainly in single rooms, with the additional use of a former staff bungalow for therapeutic groups and rehabilitation. Its role is a combination of assessment, rehabilitation, and longstay care for 'confused' physically active people whose behaviour is too difficult to be managed elsewhere. It has a sophisticated and carefully structured programme of group therapy, individual support and goal planning combined with a quite exceptional in-service staff training programme, and commitment to family involvement in care. There are interesting points of comparison with the experimental unit in High Wycombe (page 15) and also with William-wood House and Woodside.

Woodside, Birmingham—is a 30-bedded local authority home whose current official role is to provide shortstay beds for assessment and respite care, together with very flexible day care. Strictly speaking, therefore, it should not have been included in this study. For a long time, however, due to the 'silting-up' of the assessment beds, it was in practice a longstay care home. The means taken to recover its previous role as well as the potential, and problems of its present mode of operation are of considerable interest to anyone concerned in this field. In particular, its use of unqualified staff in the assessment process, its success in operating without any psychogeriatric support services, its relaxed regime, and its use as a staging post in the placement of people in non-specialist care, all have implications for this study.

National Health Service provision
Dove House, Peterborough—provides 16 longstay and six short-stay beds in a single storey building which is part of a complex mainly used for housing people with mental handicap. A similar building on the same site is used by the NHS for specialist day care. The charge nurse at Dove House is anxious to provide a domestic and relaxed lifestyle for the longstay patients, and friendly and accessible emergency and respite care. There is, however, a constant tension between these objectives and traditional NHS practice and administration, so that Dove House offers an interesting example of the difficulties likely to be encountered by the many health authorities who are seeking to provide longstay care for dementia sufferers in small localised units. Another area of interest is the relationship between Dove House and the neighbouring day hospital, and the difficulties encountered in using the latter for the benefit of longstay residents.

The Bungalow, Honiton—is a new 20-bedded unit built within the grounds of a community hospital. Intended to provide longstay, shortstay, assessment and community care facilities in the Honiton locality, it is the first completed phase of a planned strategy to close a traditional psychiatric hospital at Exminster in 1987 and relocate psychogeriatric facilities in nine different districts. Similar plans are being made for acute psychiatry and mental handicap. This pioneer project's primary interest is its planning and implementation, the degree to which it has lived up to its objectives, and the lessons the process may have for the many other authorities who are planning similar steps (see page 11).

September Ward, York House, Manchester Royal Infirmary—a longstay 28-bedded ward in a purpose-built psychogeriatric ESMI unit, is incorporated within the sprawling Manchester Royal Infirmary teaching hospital. An assessment/treatment ward (mainly for organic illness) and a very large and well-staffed day hospital are provided on the same site. It was hoped that the ward would benefit from the wide range of professional skills and sophisticated physical treatment facilities available in the hospital, and would combine these with high ideals in the provision of care. In fact, the ward is fairly traditional both in design and regime. The difficulty experienced in matching ideals to practice and the advantages and disadvantages of providing

44

long-term care on the same site as other forms of treatment are the main points of interest.

Ettrick Ward, Dingleton Hospital, Melrose—Dingleton was opened in 1872 as a traditional psychiatric hospital serving a huge rural catchment area in the Scottish Borders. Nearly half of its 336 beds are psychogeriatric, but it also offers acute and long-term psychiatric and mental handicap services. One of its psychiatric wards has been included in this study in order to compare the care given in a traditional psychiatric hospital with that provided in smaller institutions. Dingleton seemed particularly suitable for this purpose because it has a national and international reputation as the pioneer of the 'therapeutic community' model of management (in which decision-making and responsibility are shared amongst staff and patients, and are used as part of the treatment process), and because of its extensive use of hospital-based nursing staff to provide crisis intervention and continuing care in the community. It seemed that if there is a viable role for traditional psychiatric hospitals in the field of longstay psychogeriatric care, Dingleton would be able to show what it is. Ettrick Ward, which provides 28 longstay beds, has been made the main focus of the case study.

Non-statutory provision
Private sector
Highland House, Hunstanton—is a private ten-bedded residential home which operates on a very domestic pattern, the proprietor and her family being closely involved in care provision. It represents one end of the scale of 'specialised care' described in this report and the severity and nature of disability catered for at any one time varies considerably. Its main interest lies in the approach of a proprietor, whose professional training was in occupational therapy, to the management of people with dementia and behavioural disorders in a small 'guest house' type setting.

Kilncroft, Hastings—is a 27-bedded private residential home in converted premises providing specialist care. It is owned and run by a nurse with SRN/RMN training and extensive charge nurse experience and it has become the pilot scheme for a small group of specialist homes with centralised financial management and staff supervision. This group is run as a limited company called Croft. It currently has two homes established in Tunbridge Wells and Bromley and a further purpose-built one is being planned. Kilncroft is thus of interest in terms of the way in which it is managed and run; the quality of care offered; its relationship with statutory services and its position as the pioneer of a 'chain' of specialist homes.

Oxford Road Nursing Home, Southport (R & M Homes)—a three-storey private nursing home, which was registered for 30 beds at the time of the visit, adjoins a private residential home under the same ownership. A link unit between the homes, which will provide another nine beds, was under construction. The home specialises in the care of dementia sufferers, though some patients suffering from personality disorder and severe communication problems arising from physical disability are also admitted, and it is heavily used as a source of longstay places by the local psychiatric hospital. The proprietor is qualified as an RMN/RNMH. The establishment is a rare example of a private mental nursing home specialising in this field (only 14 were identified in the whole of the UK) and it also illustrates many of the problems of offering private nursing care in converted domestic housing for this client group.

Voluntary sector
Williamwood House, Glasgow—is the only residential home in Scotland which specialises in the care of elderly people with mental disability and one of the handful of *voluntary* residential homes in the whole of the UK which specialises in this way. It provides 30 places (two shortstay at present) for people suffering from moderate dementia or from other forms of mental illness, and it places strong emphasis on individualised care, normal lifestyle, rehabilitation and high activity levels. The sponsoring organisation is the Church of Scotland and there is an overtly Christian focus in the home's management. The Church of Scotland is now planning two more homes on the same lines and much interest in the management and regime has been shown by the statutory sector in Scotland.

Severity and mix of mental disability
Crichton Royal Behavioural Rating Scale
An attempt was made to assess severity of dementia in each establishment by using a simplified version of the CRBRS scale for memory, orientation and communication, which was originally devised by Robinson[1]. In its full form, residents are graded on the following basis:—

Memory

0. *Complete.* Not at all forgetful or only within range of normal expectations.

1. *Occasionally forgetful.* Forgets that he or she has done something or forgets where things have been left (eg forgets that he collected pension or that she had a bath—tendency to mislay personal possessions). But can easily be reminded and retains awareness of what happened yesterday or last week.

2. *Short-term loss.* Little idea of what happened yesterday or last week, but retains memory of more distant past. Can talk sensibly about past, not just isolated events.

3. *Short and long-term loss.* No memory or only remembers isolated events which may be confused with events which took place at a different time.

Orientation

0. *Complete.* Fully oriented in the institution and appears to have a fairly good idea of where he or she is outside (eg knows where he or she is on outings). Has reasonable understanding of current events (eg comprehends news on television). Rating may be hypothetical in cases where the person does not go out of the institution.

1. *Oriented in ward, identifies people correctly.* Easily lost outside but aware of layout of immediate surroundings. Able to recognise and name people with whom he or she has regular dealings (eg relatives and staff). Able to differentiate members of staff.

2. *Mis-identifies but can find way about.* Able to find way to bedroom and toilet without assistance, but cannot apply names to members of staff (eg calls all staff by the same name or confuses names). May still recognise one or more relatives. Ability to find way does not include wanderers who come across bedroom or toilet in their travels. If physically handicapped, and therefore unable to move around independently, should show awareness of immediate surroundings. Deafness and/or speech defects can make assessment difficult.

3. *Cannot find way to bed or toilet without assistance.* Unable to identify people and unable to find way about. Needs help finding bedroom or toilet, but may be able to find one or the other. Rate physically handicapped according to awareness of

surroundings. Must retain some idea of place, ie understands that he or she is in a home or in a hospital.

4. *Completely lost.* No idea of where he or she is. May lay down wrong way in bed, unless directed.

Communication

0. *Always clear, retains information.* Can carry on a normal conversation without the need to simplify. Able to cope with own affairs. Could go shopping if physically capable. If conversation is limited, because of deafness or speech defect, code 1.

1. *Can indicate needs, understands simple verbal directions, can deal with simple information.* Understands a simplified conversation and responds appropriately. Includes those with limited intelligence and those handicapped by speech or hearing defects.

2. *Cannot understand simple verbal information OR cannot indicate needs.* Manages one or the other, but not both. For understanding individual must respond appropriately. Needs can be indicated in other ways than by speech. Must be able to make the listener understand what is wanted (eg food, drink, toiletting etc).

3. *Cannot understand simple verbal information AND cannot indicate needs; retains some expressive ability.* Failure to understand is main criterion. Retains some expressive ability, but its inappropriateness to the conversation reveals lack of understanding. Will not ask for things, but will respond when spoken to, eg will say 'hello' when greeted.

4. *No effective contact.* Does not respond to communication. May talk, but this is unrelated to anything that is said. Will not respond to greeting or only inappropriately.

Those scoring 0–1 are categorised as 'lucid'; 2–3 'marginal'; 4–6 'moderately confused' and 7–11 'severely confused'. This sub-score of the CRBRS has been found to correspond well with clinical assessment[2].

A member of the care staff who knew the residents well (usually the OIC) was asked to rate longstay residents in accordance with their capacity under the italic title of each classification (the full

TABLE 9   CRBRS Scores

	Average	Range	No of longstay residents
Local Authority			
Bemerton Lodge Special Care Unit	5.1	4–8	10
Orchard House Flat Two	7.8	4–11	8
Bole Hill View	9.4	5–11	25
Vernon House	8.6	5–11	29 (now 27)
Ferrard House	7.7	0–11	31
NHS			
Dove House	7.1	3–11	16
The Bungalow	9.4	6–11	20
September Ward, York Hse	8.5	5–11	15 (28)*
Ettrick Ward, Dingleton Hospital	8.5	4–11	28
Non-statutory			
Highland House	4.2	0–10	10
Kilncroft	7.5	0–11	27
Oxford Rd. Nursing Home	6.8	4–11	30
Williamwood House	5.7	1–8	28

* Only 15 beds filled and staffed at the time of the visit out of a possible 28.

description was not used). Scores were totalled and divided by the number of residents to give both an average and a range for each home. The results are summarised below (Woodside was not included because of its concentration on shortstay admissions).

As the more detailed descriptions in the case studies show, these scores are misleading in that the presence of psychotic or brain-damaged residents without dementia who have a very low score can considerably reduce the average, although they may still present severe management problems, and good management can in itself reduce the score even when severe dementia is present. The level of physical disability also varies considerably and the physically active may be more difficult to manage than very disabled people. It is, however, of interest that three of the local authority homes have average scores which equal or are above the NHS establishments, although the latter include a traditional psychiatric ward and two units with 'decanted' patients from traditional hospitals. Furthermore, three out of the four NHS units contained patients who were 'lucid', 'marginal' or 'moderately confused'. Also, although all establishments, except The Bungalow, had some residents who were not classified as 'severely confused', eleven out of the thirteen also had residents who had virtually no cognitive function left (scores of 10 and 11). It is, therefore, evident that even in highly specialised units specifically coping with dementia sufferers, the population is by no means homogeneous, and while a degree of mix is probably inevitable and possibly desirable (certainly from the staff's point of view) it is a topic which we need to know much more about. This issue is dealt with further below when discussing the combination of longstay care with other forms of service provision.

In some cases the nature of the client group to be catered for is spelt out in detail by the proprietor or providing authority (Bemerton Lodge, Oxford Road, Orchard House, Williamwood House). In NHS units this is not necessary because it is taken for granted that the establishment will receive and cope with anyone whom the consultant refers, though efforts are made to move on people who prove to be suitable for a non-specialist environment. All the non-NHS units said that they could not cope with unprovoked severe aggression, especially if it endangered other residents, and some cited other forms of behaviour disorder which were also unacceptable. There was strong awareness of the need to avoid admitting people who were sufficiently alert to be distressed by the nature of the home, but there was also flexibility in allowing people to stay who had become settled even though they did not really need the facilities. All said that they would continue to care for a dying resident unless they needed hospital facilities, but had differing attitudes to chronic physical illness and disability. At Bole Hill View for example, the OIC felt strongly that the special skills of the staff lay in caring for physically-active people with severe dementia and that when the primary need was for physical tending only they should be provided for elsewhere. At Woodside the OIC distinguished between people who had become disabled and had lost control of the autonomic nervous system (lower brain functions—see page 1) as a result of dementia and those who became disabled for other reasons; Kilncroft, a three-storeyed house which had no lift at the time of the visit, could not cope with people who were likely to be immobile over a long period and would also transfer people whose dementia had become so severe that they were unaware of the nature of their environment and unable to profit from it. The private nursing home, Oxford Road, does accept all levels of physical disability until death. The fact that all the non-NHS settings were unable to manage some types of client indicates that there is either a need for a higher proportion of RMN nurses in the residential sector (as some RMN informants advocated) or that some (but very few) hospital beds will always be required to cater for severely aggressive or otherwise unmanageable people, and especially for physically and sexually active severely-demented men whose management often gave rise to most anxiety. Equally, however, as this and many other studies have shown, there are many people on hospital wards who can easily be managed in a residential setting and should certainly have been placed there in the first instance. It would seem that there is a need for a much clearer policy so that the sector in which people are cared for is not determined by the availability of a bed or the path of referral, and traditional hospital wards are used as a last resort.

Design and furnishing
Typical designs
The study has identified four different types of accommodation which have very distinct characteristics:

• *Purpose-built, single-unit local authority homes.* These are usually single-storey and those in the study were built either on the 'race track' model with a circular passage round a central courtyard (Bole Hill View, Vernon House and Ferrard House) or with dead-end passages stemming from a central point like fingers on a hand (Woodside). Race-track homes normally provide a large proportion of single rooms, ample space to 'wander', and safe access to the open air in the central courtyard. However, the never-ending passage does encourage residents to go on walking to the point of exhaustion, sometimes insisting that a less energetic resident accompanies them. The design makes it difficult for staff to oversee what is happening on the far side of the building, so that bedroom doors are often locked during the day and the central courtyard makes it necessary for the home to be fairly large with corresponding disadvantages of size for this client group, both in terms of individualised care and distance between essential facilities. Distance to sitting and dining facilities increases disorientation and adds to the staff time needed for escorting residents. The 'finger' model allows some internal segregation in different wings, but presents similar difficulties in supervision, no 'naturally' enclosed space (though this can be provided) and the possibility of frustration of residents who cannot get out at the end of the corridors.

• *Group-unit homes.* These provide a sitting/dining/kitchenette area in close association with a group of bedrooms. Orientation can be improved by using different colour schemes and decorative symbols in each unit, and the close association of different living areas makes supervision much easier. A group unit home can still be built on the race-track model so that residents can wander beyond their own 'territory' if they wish to do so, as at King's Haven in East Sussex. However most group unit homes devote only one wing to specialist care and if this is of the 'dead end' variety it may give little space for wandering and result in residents being at very close quarters when sitting and eating (Orchard House). In these circumstances, unpleasant noisy or aggressive behaviour may become difficult to manage. A carefully planned, purpose-built wing built onto an established home can eliminate many of these problems and in this regard the Special Unit at Bemerton Lodge with its large central open space and surrounding bedrooms, may well be taken as a model.

• *Ward-like units.* All the modern local authority building seen in the course of the study is in strong contrast to that provided by the NHS whose architects seem unable to free themselves from the concept of the traditional hospital ward. Even brand new localised units, such as September Ward in York House and The Bungalow at Honiton, are set out in the traditional pattern with wards, day room, nursing station and strongly clinical atmosphere. The ward cubicles may have slightly more furniture than is usually provided in a hospital, and the cubicle curtains and bedspreads may be of attractive material, but there is no door which the patient can shut on the world; washing facilities are shared, and it is extremely difficult for busy staff to ensure that privacy and dignity are maintained.

The advantages of this model are that it facilitates the provision of physical care, it enables constant observation and it gives staff confidence because they are working in a familiar environment where everything can be kept under control. But it also encourages staff to see people as 'patients' with all that this implies in depersonalisation, loss of self-determination and loss of self-care skills.

• *Converted private houses.* Much specialist provision in both local authorities and health authorities is purpose-built. In the private sector the reverse is true and the three private establishments observed in this study were all converted multi-storey houses with living accommodation on the ground floor; and bedrooms (many of them shared) upstairs. It is not at all easy to provide good care in this setting. The lounge and dining space, like the 'wings' of Part III homes, are cramped and give little opportunity for movement or activities. The bedrooms are often little used during the day because of anxiety about supervision and falls on the stairs, which may indeed be closed off by gates, and there is no opportunity for personal privacy within the shared rooms. On the other hand, these homes are often set in the context of a normal street, they are relatively domestic in scale, and they can provide a much less institutional environment than large purpose-built NHS or local authority establishments. Williamwood House has the best of both worlds in that its lounge, dining and office provision is on the ground floor of a spacious modern mansion and its bedroom wing is purpose-built with one floor on a level with the main house. That, however, is a model which cannot easily be imitated.

Size of homes

The received opinion is that 'small is beautiful' and that it is much easier to provide individualised and personal care in a familiar and domestic setting for six or eight severely dependent people than for a larger number. Certainly, the nature and quality of the care being provided in the two 'wing' units visited bears this out. However, these units are viable because they draw heavily on the resources of the main home, not only in terms of management, catering, cleaning and maintenance, but also because in both cases the senior staff of the homes give a great deal of time and effort to selecting, training and supporting the staff in the specialist units.

'Free-standing', small, specialist units in both the statutory sectors would be not only costly but vulnerable, and a great deal of thought would need to be given to their support and management. On the other hand, larger units undoubtedly do create their own problems from the sheer weight and stress of concentrated disability; the pressure to provide nothing but physical care increases with numbers; and the skills of the senior staff are taken up by administration rather than by direct involvement in improving the quality of care. Thus, running an institution of the size of Bole Hill View is a major administrative task in its own right (the more so, as no secretarial help is provided).

Many of the problems arising from small-scale provision in the statutory sector can be minimised if the longstay facility is combined with day care, respite care and the provision of a 'community resource' service, but, as is discussed further on page 73, provision of such services from one site is not necessarily to the advantage of longstay residents since it drains off staff attention and time to more obviously rewarding parts of the work. A complex group of factors have to be juggled when considering optimum size in any particular situation, but if the accommodation is spacious enough, the 'wing' solution certainly seems to provide one of the best answers.

In the private sector, a financially viable size is essential to survival, but this varies according to the capital debt on the premises and current government policy on the level of fees payable by social security. Although 'small' may be 'beautiful' it is extremely difficult to staff a private home at a level which cares adequately for people with severe dementia unless there are at least 16 residents. Highland House, the smallest home in this study, is only viable because the proprietor virtually gives all her own time and is on 24-hour call.

Another factor which it is important to bear in mind is the use to which the building can be put if it is no longer required for dementia sufferers. Concepts of, and the need for, institutional care do not remain static, and outmoded buildings either perpetuate service provision of a particular type long after it has ceased to be seen as desirable, or remain as expensive white elephants for which some use has to be found. The Victorian psychiatric hospitals are a prime example of this, but we have seen the same syndrome in the field of residential care for children and in care for physically and mentally handicapped people. Improvements in service provision should make it possible for more and more people with dementia to remain in their own homes, and it is quite possible that a means of preventing, curing or stabilising the illness will be found in the reasonably near future. From this point of view, linked bungalows, which can easily revert to domestic use, may be much more economic in the long run than other types of purpose-built homes, as well as being more normal and 'domestic' in style and in relationship to other housing stock. Potential flexibility of use is also important in allocating space for the development of homes as resource centres, with office room for staff who are involved in community care; respite and day care facilities, and friendly, easy access for carers who need help and advice[3].

54

General design considerations

All the observations on design and furnishing made in *Bricks and mortals*[4] are relevant to specialist homes. Bathroom and lavatory accommodation needs to be suitable for use by very disabled people; furniture needs to be free-standing to encourage flexibility in the use of rooms and the introduction of personal items; much can be done to create a sense of individuality in resident's rooms through imaginative use of bedcovers, rugs, curtains and pictures; and dignity and comfort in the dining room are just as important as in the lounge—a good dining room can make a valuable activity area, especially if movement between sitting, dining and kitchen space is natural and easy. One key aspect of design is the use made of the 'hotel foyer' concept of 'public space'. People, whether they suffer from dementia or not, like to sit in an area where there is plenty of coming and going, and where there is natural opportunity for staff contact. Thus, sitting space at the entrance of Bole Hill View, Vernon House, and Woodside was always fully used, and in Bemerton Lodge Special Unit the door end of the sitting space was the most used. The importance of a large, attractive accessible office which is not 'defended' against residents also cannot be over-emphasised. In fact the interaction between residents and staff on staff 'territory' is probably one of the best single indicators of the way in which a home is run (for example Bole Hill View, Williamwood and Woodside). An alternative, tried successfully in Bemerton Lodge, is to have a very small office for the telephone and essential paperwork *outside* the unit with an inconspicuous connecting window, but to encourage all other staff activity and interaction to take place alongside the residents.

Little has been said in this report about the use of signs and colours to encourage orientation. Most establishments do label lavatories and residents' rooms and some have particular colours in particular corridors, or put distinctive pictures on bedroom doors, though there is always a potential conflict between creating an institutional atmosphere with too much labelling and helping residents to find their way about. Some attempts to improve orientation have proved to be positively confusing. It was found at Woodside, for example, that heavy black lines of tiles leading to the WCs were mistaken by residents for steps, with consequent falls. In general, it seems important that the *overall* design of a home should minimise confusion as much as possible (there is nothing worse than a badly-designed, race-track home in this regard) and that orientation should then be encouraged by relatively unobtrusive and 'adult' means. For people suffering from really severe dementia any such measures will, in any case, be of little use.

Single rooms
Do people with severe dementia profit from having single rooms? This is a basic question when considering design. Those who say 'no' argue that people who may have been accustomed to sharing a room with a spouse for most of their lives are more settled and more secure in shared accommodation, and that they are less likely to get up at an inappropriate time. Also it is said that they are so unaware of their surroundings that they do not feel loss of privacy, and that heavy physical care is easier to provide. However, it was noteworthy that the exponents of shared bedrooms were mainly the private proprietors who offered this type of accommodation. No-one running a home with a large number of single rooms advocated sharing, although the single rooms were rarely individualised and staff often expressed the wish to do more in this direction, or to encourage relatives to do so. The overriding argument in favour of single rooms for this client group is that privacy is a basic attribute of free and responsible adults. Children, prisoners, soldiers and 'patients' may sleep in dormitories or shared rooms. People in their own homes are considered to be statutorily 'overcrowded' if they are forced to do so. Staff looking after residents who have their own rooms are much more likely to perceive them as individuals with a right to privacy and respect, and the seclusion of the bedroom is the natural place to provide physical care. Further, single rooms make it much easier to look after people with a wide range of mental disabilities and to provide respite and assessment services alongside longstay residents without causing distress. Single rooms and flexible use go together.

The same argument applies to furniture and furnishings. Whether or not residents are able to perceive high quality (and they can certainly perceive comfort and attractive colours), *staff* see generous and careful provision as reflecting the value put on residents and therefore on the staff's work with them. It is psychologically extremely difficult to provide good care in surroundings of which you are ashamed.

Individuality[5]
This concept focuses on ways in which each resident is recognised

and treated as an individual and given maximum help in retaining their personality and their relationships. It can be further broken down in terms of identity, personal relationships, maintenance of established skills and habits, and provision of individual care plans.

Identity

The basis of 'identity' is a knowledge of the personal history and home background of the person concerned. The homes visited were very variable in this regard. Poor knowledge and skimpy records are understandable in relation to establishments which provide for people who have been in hospital for many years, but poor information provided by field social workers also results in very sketchy records in local authority homes, and staff frequently complained that they had to build up what information they could from the resident and relatives after admission. Information collected in this way was not often systematically written down and therefore not easily picked up by new staff. The best practice in this regard was observed at Williamwood House where the key worker has a responsibility for making a 'pen portrait' of the resident; at Orchard House, where one of the care staff is creating a detailed 'life history book' for each resident: and at Ferrard House, where a very detailed description of daily living habits is compiled for each new resident. Kilncroft asks for photographs of residents before they became ill as part of the admission procedure and puts them up, with a couple of lines of biographical details, on a board in the dining room. There would seem to be no reason why relatives should not routinely be asked to supply a written history and any 'illustrations' as part of the admission process, which would in itself help to demonstrate to them the home's concern with the new resident as a person.

The same point needs to be made about personal possessions. For those who have come from other institutions, these may again be minimal, but people coming from their own homes must have had many more familiar objects to bring with them than were observed in the course of the study; even in establishments where most residents had their own rooms, and where it was official policy for residents to bring in their own furniture and other possessions. Again there were exceptions; Williamwood spells out the personal necessities which everyone is expected to bring with them, and some residents also bring a lot of personal furniture. Orchard House also does well in this regard, and one room of Highland House is filled with a collection of shells given to a resident by her son. At Kilncroft one resident proudly displays a large stuffed, rat-like creature which belonged to an explorer husband. There are, of course, risks over loss and breakage of possessions, but it seems possible that the more individual a room is, the less this is likely to happen. Certainly the special unit at Welland House Peterborough (a new SSD group unit home not included in the case studies) has rooms filled with residents' possessions, including fragile china in a glass-fronted cabinet and models made as a hobby, and so far these have presented no problems. As in the argument given above for providing single rooms, it is important for *staff* to see residents as people with possessions as well as for residents to have them.

Another aspect of identity is the form of address used. Most of the admission forms seem to have a space for 'preferred name', but most often a first name or diminutive is used. 'Darling' and 'dear' are employed a good deal and in some cases residents were addressed as infants—'there's a good girl'—though this was pleasingly uncommon. Some homes, however, do use first names for some residents and surname with title for others, and this was fairly common with shortstay and day residents. The use of first names between new acquaintances is so common nowadays that it may seem unnecessary to question the habit in specialist homes. However, it has to be remembered that this generation of residents is not so accustomed to it (especially when it is between a young person and someone much older), unless permission has been expressly given. Moreover, for people with a failing memory the use of their title and surname can act as a positive reinforcement of their own sense of identity and adult status. Use of names also affects staff attitudes. It is quite difficult to say 'now be a good girl, Mrs Brown'. There would seem to be a strong case for very careful consideration to be given to usage in this regard. It would do no harm, for example, if names and titles were always used at handover sessions, and if new residents were called by their surname until it became clear that they responded better and preferred it if a first name was used. Junior care staff and domestics might well always be required to use surnames.

Personal relationships
This includes encouraging continued contact with family and

friends, with members of staff, with other residents, and with some kind of external 'advocate' if there is no family or friend to play this role. All the homes included in the study had totally flexible visiting hours and gave time and trouble to making contact with relatives through involving them in parties, excursions and fund-raising events. Some run a relatives' group as part of the service provided by the home (Bole Hill View, September Ward and Williamwood House) or encourage relatives to join the local Alzheimer's Disease Society (Bemerton Lodge and Dove House). Contact with relatives is likely to be particularly close if the home has been used for day care and respite care before the clients become longstay; a home visit by staff and use of a key worker in the admission process also helps to establish a positive contact from the start. In some homes, staff will accompany a resident and relative on a visit or outing if the latter is uncertain about being able to manage alone. Considerable awareness was expressed by staff of relatives' need for: support after they had ceased to provide physical care at home and their need to come to terms with bereavement, guilt and loss of role; the importance of enabling them to continue to share in the caring without becoming obsessional through an inability to 'let go'; their value in supporting each other, and especially the relatives of potential residents; their contribution to events which require one-to-one support of residents; and their value in enabling staff to find out more about a resident's history, personality, and tastes. It was also recognised that staff may play a key role in enabling a relative to feel reasonably comfortable on a visit and to feel that it is worth the trouble, even if the resident does not recognise them, or immediately forgets that they have been, or becomes distressed when they leave. Much more staff training and help with dealing with their own feelings about relatives is needed and the OIC at Williamwood has written a perceptive internal staff training paper in this regard.

Contact with friends can also be encouraged through helping the resident to maintain some links with former activities—religious, social or sporting—and this is discussed further below. It also helps if, during the admission process, information is obtained about the names and addresses of people with whom the resident is in contact so that greeting cards, letters, photographs and so on can be sent when this is appropriate. It is very easy for people in any form of longstay care to fall into social death, and reminders that they are alive and active are important. The response which such cards and letters elicit also helps to remind both resident and staff that the person concerned is still part of a complex and caring social network.

Much has been said in the case studies about the role of a key worker. The Bungalow, Orchard House, Williamwood House, Ferrard House and Woodside provide interesting examples of the varied use of this concept. Although details vary, key workers have three principal roles: they conduct the admission process, with all that entails; they get to know a resident's history, tastes, habits and personality on a really detailed level; and they plan the means whereby lifestyle can be maintained, skills used and realistic goals achieved. They should, however, provide a bridge for involvement and relationships with other staff rather than being seen as 'owning' the resident, and the key worker system should not allow other care staff to feel that the resident's well-being is none of their business. It is also necessary to have an 'opposite number' or 'support worker' who will take particular responsibility when the key worker is not on duty. Given these safeguards, the concept seems to be a very valuable one, but it does have implications for training which are discussed further below.

Relationships between residents have not been much discussed in this study, but they are of importance in homes in which the level of disability is not so severe that real interaction has become impossible (Bemerton Lodge, Highland House, Ferrard House, Kilncroft and Williamwood House) and even when the level is very severe partnerships can become established. Sensitive encouragement of constructive developments of this kind is important.

Even when highly motivated, staff find it difficult to stand back and look at the way in which they are providing care, especially when this is over a long period. Residents who do not have a member of their family in close contact to observe and comment on care provision and take part in reviews do, therefore, need a volunteer 'advocate' who will take the role of a family member in visiting, befriending and speaking for them. This should not be seen as a role of criticism or confrontation, but rather as a partnership with staff to make sure that the resident is leading as full and happy a life as possible. None of the homes in the study had such a system, though the local committee of William-wood goes some way towards it. CPA is currently involved in the experimental provision of an advocacy service in non-specialist homes, and the King's Fund Centre report[6] includes a brief discussion of its relevance in this field, as well as that of mental handicap. Much more work needs to be done in this area.

Skills and interests
Mention has already been made of the importance of maintaining individuality by building on established interests and social contacts, both in terms of going out to a church, a pub, or a football match and in terms of using former skills within the home even if the end result is not of much practical use. Restless, agitated people may become contented if they have some dough to knead or are given a duster and something to polish, or a patch of ground to dig, especially if they are working alongside the 'real' worker (which is one reason why domestics, cooks, handymen and gardeners are such important members of staff), and the individuality of the person concerned can shine through as they find themselves in an accustomed role. Maintenance of self care skills is discussed further in the next section, but the point needs to be made that this is impossible unless the staff member knows what the long-established habits are and finds means of supporting them. The detailed lists of personal habits and customs compiled at Williamwood and Ferrard House are valuable examples of the sort of knowledge which is needed.

Individual care plans
Homes in the study varied considerably in whether they made a care plan for each resident and also the degree to which they were able to follow it and review progress. The most detailed care plan was found at Orchard House with a careful analysis of areas in which change is desirable, its feasibility, and who needs to change, followed by a breakdown of the nature of the problem and the steps needed to tackle it. Williamwood and Ferrard House have similar but less detailed systems while The Bungalow and September Ward have an ambitious monitoring system which is not yet being fully used.

The key word here would seem to be 'realism'. It is easy enough to identify 'problem' areas relating to continence, self care skills, agitation, mobility, orientation and so on, and record vague intentions about their improvement, but the vaguer and more ambitious the objective the less likely it is that it will be achieved. It is also necessary to face the fact that the resident is likely, over a period, to deteriorate rather than improve, and the goal may need to be to maintain existing skills rather than recover lost ones. Very simple goals in widening an area of choice—for example in spending money, selecting clothing or having an enjoyable bath—may be more realistic and pleasant for both resident and staff member than focusing on a lost skill which then becomes a 'problem' because it has been defined as such. At this level of disability, the emphasis must always be on enhancing the enjoyment of the individual rather than on trying to force the recovery of skills which may have irrevocably gone.

Choice

Ability to exercise choice and self-determination in daily living is another key component in the provision of good care and was used as the touchstone in compiling the checklist on which *Bricks and mortals*[7] is based. It is no less important in the field of specialist care, but much vigilance and hard work is needed to make it possible. This section reviews the operation of choice in relation to sleep, continence, bathing, clothing, eating, movement and the use of money.

Getting up and going to bed

Most establishments in the study have managed to create a relaxed and flexible regime in the getting up process (in stark contrast to many 'ordinary' residential homes). Some residents are naturally early risers and some like to sleep till 10.00 or 11.00 am, an uncooked breakfast being provided when they are ready for it. The most rigid routines were found in Kilncroft and Oxford Road, where the need to bring residents down from the upper floors and keep them under supervision results in an early start and 'batch' treatment. The same problem would be encountered in Highland House, but the relatively high ability of residents means that they can be given breakfast in bed and then got up and brought down at leisure. Another cause for concern is the gap in some establishments between getting up and breakfast. Residents may sit and doze in the lounge or around the breakfast table for an hour or more, usually with TV AM blaring in the corner and often with a strong smell of urine from wet bedclothes wafting along the passages. It is the most depressing moment of the day. It is far better when the system allows all but the earliest risers to be served with breakfast as soon as they are ready, although waiting is not so bad if the surroundings are homely, the TV is switched off, and tea is available.

The dressing process was rightly conducted in privacy and no attempt was made to intrude on it, so this important opportunity to encourage self help and provide consistent care remained unobserved. Most establishments emphasise the need to offer choice to residents in what they wear, and the importance of encouraging self care, but one suspects that in many of the larger specialist units the need for speed obviates this in practice. The only detailed instructions to staff in this regard were found at Williamwood and Woodside. The need for a choice to be made at Oxford Road between starting to get residents up at 5.30 am and dressing them downstairs after breakfast seemed particularly regrettable. The process of going to bed was also reasonably flexible in most places. The main contrast was between units which expected that everyone would be in bed by 10.00 or 10.30 pm and established their routine accordingly, and those where there was a genuinely open choice. Highland House, Dove House, Williamwood and Woodside were particularly free in this regard.

Night sedation seemed to be genuinely little used (though lack of expertise relating to drugs made this difficult to check), but there was a wide and unexplained variation in the amount of night restlessness and wandering. In Orchard House, for example, despite an early bedtime, the very severely disabled clientele could apparently be left all night with only occasional checks from staff who were responsible for the whole home. However at Vernon House and Woodside the night is nearly as active as the day. There is a need for more investigation of the reasons for this, and of other aspects of night-time care (see below).

Management of continence
It was noteworthy that control of incontinence had become so much a matter of routine in the establishments visited that it had ceased to be seen as a problem. There was very little smell, carpetting was successfully maintained in lounge areas, and dignity was usually well supported. However, the method used to achieve the end varied considerably, and this seemed to be determined by numbers and customary practice as much as by mental disability in the group concerned. Some establishments combine a liberal use of pads with two-hourly toiletting, or routine adapted to observed need (Bole Hill View, Vernon House, Dove House, Dingleton and Highland House); some use pads if required, but put emphasis on keeping a detailed chart for all residents and adapting routine to individual habits (Kilncroft, Woodside and September Ward); and some are able to manage with minimal routine or use of pads and no general chart, but require detailed staff observation of individuals when necessary (Bemerton Lodge, Orchard House, Williamwood).

There is a similar variation at night: only Kilncroft kept firmly to the traditional hospital routine of a two-hourly 'check' and a 2.00 am toilet round. Several establishments attempt to observe individual patterns of night-time micturition and establish a routine to suit them (September Ward, Oxford Road, Orchard House, Ferrard House, Williamwood and Bemerton Lodge). Both practices may be combined with use of pads and some form of incontinence sheet. At Woodside all residents are left to sleep undisturbed and pads are extensively used. There is an interesting conflict between the benefit of having an undisturbed night; the benefit and dignity of staying 'dry'; and the benefit and dignity of not reverting to the infantile practice of wearing incontinence pads. Individual need is probably the best guide, but we should know much more about the advantages and disadvantages of each practice.

Bathing
Again, there are considerable variations in practice which do not directly relate to facilities or level of disability. Some establishments try to establish a personal preference for time and frequency (Highland House, Ferrard House, Orchard House and Williamwood); some keep a bath book which is adhered to as a matter of routine unless a bath is required more often (Dove House, Dingleton, Kilncroft and Oxford Road); some leave the giving of baths to the judgement of the key worker or 'corridor staff' (Bole Hill View, Vernon House and The Bungalow) and some are very dependent on the necessary staff being available and operate an *ad hoc* system (Bemerton Lodge, September Ward). Bathroom accommodation tends to be particularly inadequate in the local authority homes. Perhaps the actual bathing process, and whether or not the resident enjoys it, are more important than the type of routine. Allaying fears; ensuring that a familiar routine is adhered to; giving time to 'soak' if this is enjoyed; encouraging self care; and the use of pleasant toiletries are all matters of importance. Highland House and Williamwood seemed to be leaders in this respect.

Clothing
It was comforting to find that concern about provision of good quality and dignified personal clothing, properly marked and laundered, was found in all the establishments visited and, in spite of the difficulties, they largely succeeded in achieving this. (Communal night clothing was, however, still being used in several of the NHS establishments.) Means of purchase included

shopping expeditions with the resident, clothes bought on approval by staff, clothes bought by relatives, visiting salesmen, and the use of a wholesaler to provide made-to-measure dresses.

The challenge is not only to offer choice at the point of purchase, but to ensure that clothes fit personality and previous taste and to maintain them in good order. There is also the need to ensure that choice is offered at the point of dressing; that self care in this regard is achieved as far as possible; that customary make-up, and good skin and nail care are maintained; and that necklaces and brooches are worn by those who like them. Clothing worn by staff is also important. This ranged in the establishments visited from traditional nursing uniform, through simple overalls to ordinary clothing. The two extremes meet at The Bungalow, with some nurses still insisting on their uniform and others luxuriating in the brightest of Fair Isle sweaters. There are two aspects to this issue: one is that the wearing of a uniform by staff clearly establishes that they are a different order of being from patients or residents; it is a statement of superiority and authority rather than a practical convenience as is shown by the ease with which it can be abandoned. The other aspect is that there was clear evidence that people with severe dementia noticed and appreciated what staff were wearing. On several occasions during the visits, they were heard to comment with pleasure on the colour, feel the texture of a dress or skirt, or say that they would like something similar. In a situation where contact with the 'ordinary' world is so limited, the opportunity for every experience of this kind needs to be maximised.

Finally, a word needs to be said about protective clothing for residents at meal times. Again practice was very varied, both in type of apron worn and whether or not it was put on regardless of need. The range goes from very institutional-looking plastic aprons of a uniform colour, via thin disposable polythene ones identical to those used by staff when doing dirty jobs, to bright, individual vinyl cooking aprons. There is no perfect answer to this, but thought does need to be given to ensuring they are as non-infantile, suitable and inconspicuous as possible.

Provision of meals
No establishment was without at least a pantry/kitchen, and this facility should be considered essential in any new building. Without it, it is not possible to provide staggered breakfasts or to meet individual needs for a snack at any time of the day or night.

Even with this provision, however, establishments are limited in flexibility of timing and choice of meals if they are dependent on a main kitchen to provide them, and the bigger and more remote the kitchen the more this is true (though Ferrard House would claim to be an exception). The private sector comes out well here, with the kitchens at Kilncroft and Highland House being particularly accessible and able to respond to individual need. It was noteworthy that in both cases care staff were involved in food preparation—indeed, at Highland House, they did all the cooking. The means of involving residents in cooking and washing-up activities in a natural 'non-OT' kind of way is also of basic importance. Williamwood, Bemerton Lodge, Highland House and Orchard House were all notable in this respect.

Timing of meals (apart from breakfast) tended to depend on the routine of the main kitchen, staff dining facilities, domestic staff hours, and similar administrative factors, rather than residents' needs. In particular, the evening meal everywhere seemed to be served at a time when residents were not really ready for a cooked 'tea'. Some establishments were much more flexible than others in their ability to provide a late evening snack. Most made a good attempt to cater for personal tastes in terms of likes and dislikes, ability to chew, need for a special diet and so on, and a number could offer choice between two alternatives at the point of service. However, when meals came from an impersonal main kitchen catering for other age groups, they were not always appropriate to the appetite, taste or chewing power of the recipients, and even when provision was on a more domestic scale, there was little attempt to ascertain and provide favourite foods except for an occasional and much appreciated 'fish and chip supper'. The *Bricks and mortals*[8] study found that involving Bury residents in menu planning resulted in foods such as 'steak and cowheel pie', broth with dumplings and crumpets being provided instead of pasties and quiches. Careful questioning of relatives and residents might well disclose equally strong preferences amongst this client group in spite of their dementia.

Very severe and long-standing dementia may eventually affect ability to swallow, and in a number of establishments there were residents who needed to be fed using liquidised food. This is a very distressing final stage of the illness and staff need training and support in coping with it. More common, however, is the stage at which normal perceptions and social skills have been lost and residents need a lot of personal help in eating appropriately and not interfering with other people's food. Discreet management, so that unpleasant habits do not spoil other people's enjoyment of the meal, and the disabled resident does not become frustrated and upset, is important. By and large, the homes visited did well in this difficult area, but again it is a field in which more sharing of practical ideas and skills would be very valuable.

Surroundings are nearly as important as food for the enjoyment of meals, and here conditions varied between the 'drab institutional', the 'domestic but cramped' and the 'pleasant and attractive', with Williamwood House and Bemerton Lodge leading the field (but also having the least disabled residents). Attractive high-quality furniture, bright table-cloths, and tables laid according to residents' ability to cope with cutlery etc, are very important. Ability to cope should not be under-estimated; several people reported their surprise at finding how well residents managed in hotels and pubs when on holiday and how they responded to the social expectations engendered by that situation.

Safety and restraint
Hardly anyone in the establishments visited was subject to the compulsory care or treatment provisions of the *Mental Health Act* or the *National Assistance Act*, and their carers therefore had no legal right to limit freedom of movement in any way. In most cases, however, they took it for granted that their responsibility to protect from physical harm outweighed residents' rights to freedom to come and go at will. This was true of all three private proprietors, whose homes opened almost directly onto town streets, and who saw it as their duty to protect residents by locking the front door. Of the NHS units Ettrick Ward's doors were secured with double handles and September Ward by an electric pushbutton system, but Dove House and The Bungalow relied on distance from a main road and staff observation to prevent dangerous wandering.

In the local authority sector, the group units did not need to lock doors because egress was via the main home and could therefore be prevented. Vernon House, Ferrard House and Woodside did lock the front door, and this was particularly noticeable in Woodside which otherwise operates a very relaxed regime. In contrast Bole Hill View and Williamwood kept their front doors unlocked as a matter of principle, but at Williamwood the distance from the main road provided a safeguard. Thus, of all fourteen establishments, only Bole Hill View combined proximity to a dangerous road with determined adherence to an open-door policy. The OIC here said that residents who did go out did not appear to be in danger from traffic, or to be a traffic hazard, and sometimes went right across Sheffield without coming to harm; the worst injury incurred had been from severe sunburn! However, the front door is disguised as a window by the use of a curtain, and the position of the staff office does enable a fairly good watch to be kept.

It is surprising that with this determined defence of residents' right to go out, Bole Hill did find it necessary to bolt bedroom doors during the day in order to prevent interference by other residents (as did Dove House), while in Oxford Road access to the stairs, and therefore to most of the bedrooms, was controlled by gates. Building designs which make safety or proper super-vision impossible without restricting access to personal space are obviously unsatisfactory, and this needs to be kept in mind when considering new projects. None of the establishments found it necessary to make use of 'geriatric chairs', which prevent residents from getting up through use of a tilt-back mechanism, or fixed trays, but some units catering for people with severe physical disability were beginning to acquire Kirton chairs (a type of deep armchair which is comfortable but prevents the sitter from falling forward involuntarily). Large bean-bags were also found to suit some very disabled people who could not sit comfortably in ordinary chairs. All the homes professed to make minimal use of daytime sedation when this was required, and not to use enough to cause drowsiness. This certainly appeared to be true and is important evidence that people with severe dementia *can* be managed without recourse to such measures. However, there is an urgent and widely-recognised need for a legal procedure to make it possible for medically-necessary treatment to be provided for dementia sufferers who cannot give informed consent, and which also sets out in what circumstances, if any, an individual's liberty of movement may lawfully be restricted. The present 'grey' legal situation is forcing care staff to act unlawfully, both in what they see as their residents' best interests and also in defence of their own professional reputation and peace of mind. It also results in residents' rights to choice and free movement being unnecessarily restricted.

Use of money
None of the establishments gave residents free access to their personal allowance, though there was wide variation in the use

made of it and the extent to which it was used for personal needs as opposed to collective enjoyments. Only Williamwood included enhanced skills in the use of money as part of the rehabilitation programme for some residents. When relatives kept control of the allowance, there was considerable variation in the extent to which they used it for the resident's benefit, and a social worker in Southport believed that in some cases it was used by relatives to supplement fees in the private sector, so that the resident had no personal spending money at all. When health or social services authorities kept control, staff were normally responsible for withdrawing cash from the account to buy clothing and luxuries, but there was no system which provided a check on the extent to which the money was being fully used on behalf of the resident, or which distinguished between appropriate use and expenditure which should be the responsibility of the providing authority. Almost everywhere it seemed that greater comforts in the form of luxury toiletries, furnishing, pictures, or special food could have been provided. There is clearly a need, as has been stated again and again by CPA in other contexts[9], and also by the DHSS, Mencap, MIND, Age Concern and many other organisations, for a clear set of guidelines about the proper use of the personal allowance when people are not able to manage it for themselves, and a system which ensures that it is spent in ways which bring maximum pleasure and benefit to its owners.

Activities
'Daily living' activities inevitably take up much of the day in a specialist home: the bigger the establishment the more time they take up because of the time needed to move residents from one situation to another. There was general agreement amongst informants that occupation of this kind is not enough, but there were differences of opinion about the rationale and best means of providing other activities, and also differences in the extent to which ideals live up to practice. Organised activity can be broken down into three main types—in-house activities (with or without specific therapeutic intention), outings and holidays.

Organised in-house activities
Organised in-house activities include the use of old skills and individual occupations such as reading and knitting for those who retain some capacity for this; small group games such as dominoes, ludo or snakes and ladders; 'reminiscence' sessions using photographs or objects to promote recall; 'reality orientation' sessions to reinforce awareness of current events and

the present situation; music and movement of one kind or another; singing, painting, dancing, 'quizzes' and so on. Two of the private establishments in the study, Oxford Road and Kilncroft, stress the inclusion of sessions of such activities in their daily timetable and are firm believers in its therapeutic value, though neither have yet established it to a level and quality which they would like. Bemerton Lodge, Ferrard House and Williamwood also lay great stress on their full day's programme of events. Three units—September Ward, Dove House and Bole Hill View—have associated day centres on the same premises which, in theory, means that staff from the day centres are available to provide activities to longstay residents, or that residents can use the facilities available. Desirable as this looks in theory, it does not seem to work out well in practice. The day centre staff are often reluctant to leave it and spend their time and skills on less rewarding longstay residents, and may also restrict their admission to the day centre or require them to be accompanied by staff who cannot in fact be spared. It is evident that there needs to be a very firm allocation of therapeutic staff time to the longstay group if this tendency is to be resisted.

Some of the establishments visited have neither this facility nor much in the way of other organised daytime occupation—apart from the ubiquitous TV or recorded music, both of which may be used to give the illusion of 'activity'. In some instances staff do spend quite a lot of time in informal one-to-one interaction, but inevitably this tends to favour residents who are able to respond.

Clearly, given determination, hard work and sufficient staff, a great deal can be done to generate activities, but there are a number of issues of principle involved which need more careful consideration than they usually receive. First, the defencelessness of people with severe dementia and the need to respect previous personality and lifestyle make it necessary to ask how far one should push people into occupations which they would once have found childish and demeaning. If they now enjoy, tolerate or are thought to benefit from them, is this sufficient justification? Are such activities in fact always for the benefit of the residents, or are they to enable the staff to feel they are 'doing something'? And if the latter is true, is that necessarily a bad thing, given the frustrations of their task? Can activities be made more 'adult' in the way that 'music and movement' at Woodside has become an evening party? What can be achieved by careful grouping of residents according to ability for some activities, as at Bemerton Lodge and Ferrard House? Are the products of artwork and collage discreetly hung so that the home does not present a 'kindergarten' appearance to visitors?—and so on. Above all, it needs to be remembered that the activity is there for the resident and not vice versa.

Activities outside the home
Activities outside the home are equally important. A number of establishments in the study owned, or had access to, a minibus and found this very valuable in providing for a weekly drive to familiar places round the countryside, perhaps with a stop for a pub lunch (Bole Hill View, Orchard House, Williamwood) as well as more ambitious day trips. Others organised more occasional visits to stately homes, zoos, parks and seaside resorts (Kilncroft, Bemerton Lodge, Dove House, September Ward) or made use of private cars owned by staff to take individual residents out for a shopping trip, a visit to a restaurant or a local drive. (Dove House holds an orange disabled persons parking badge for this purpose.) Where homes are within easy reach of facilities, residents may also be taken out on foot. Alternatively a taxi is sometimes hired. Several establishments put more emphasis on activities of this kind than on home-based 'pastimes', seeing them as more stimulating, as involving the resident in the 'ordinary world' and being closer to previous lifestyle. Units with this approach include Ettrick Ward at Dingleton, Woodside, Dove House and Bole Hill View, though the various forms of activity are of course not mutually exclusive. Such individual outings, however desirable, are expensive in terms of staff time and demand a considerable overlap of shifts. They also require skill, care and good public relations and it is important that a resident is not distressed by being brought into a situation which is frightening and bewildering—for example, during a pre-Christmas shopping rush. Much more could be done to involve people in accustomed activities outside the home if old friends or a competent volunteer could be persuaded to accompany them to a church, an accustomed pub, a football or cricket match, or any other place where memories of a previous lifestyle could be reactivated.

Holidays
Finally, something needs to be said about holidays. It might be thought that holidays would be disorienting for people with severe dementia and impossible for staff in terms of ensuring acceptable social behaviour. In fact, the three establishments

which do organise holidays—Dingleton, Dove House and Orchard House—report with enthusiasm on the way in which residents respond to life in a small group with higher staff ratios, a domestic environment and increased social demands. The experience is also said to benefit staff who gain greater appreciation of what their clients are capable of and also some realisation of the strain of 24-hour care which the families of severely disabled people endure. Holiday chalets seem to provide the best accommodation for people with dementia, since the scale minimises 'confusion', upholstery can be covered with incontinence sheets, and the daily living pattern can be geared to the group involved. The success of these ventures indicates that they should be common to all establisments and also that if the 'holiday situation' could be maintained in terms of staff level and normalised lifestyle for the rest of the year, residents would benefit considerably. This is another argument for small, well-staffed units of care.

'Image'
How staff perceive residents
The concept of 'image', which is not easy to put into words, is fundamental to the subject matter of this report. It is an amalgamation of all the aspects of building, furnishing, daily routine and staff behaviour which show how the care providers see the people they are providing for and whether they regard them as adults with adult rights, or as elderly children, or even, as was suggested to the author in a personal communication, as domestic animals requiring food, opportunity for appropriate micturition and defecation, exercise and petting. Aspects of building design, furnishing, daily routine and activity which reflect this 'image' have been discussed in the previous sections. There are, however, more subtle indicators. Do pictures, noticeboards and exhibitions of 'art' indicate that this is not really a home and not lived in by adults? Does constant television, left on regardless of the subject matter and often at high volume, indicate that staff need to escape the fact that silence and inactivity are a necessary part of life in very old age, or that it does not really matter what the captive population in the lounge are exposed to? (On one occasion the programme was an abstruse Open University lecture on physics.) Does the language which staff use, not only in speaking *to* residents but also in speaking *about* them, reflect denigrating or infantilising attitudes? How do staff cope with their own inevitable exasperation, frustration and exhaustion?

How employers perceive staff
Of equal importance are indicators of how the staff are themselves
regarded both within the establishment and by line management.
Are the domestics and care staff themselves properly paid, with
reasonable conditions of service, proper job descriptions and
good working conditions? Is their work recognised as being
skilled and difficult? Are they encouraged to use their initiative
and accept responsibility? Do they have access to training and to
individual supervision sessions? Are they proud of what they are
doing? Is there a career structure? The same questions need to
be asked for more senior staff, with particular emphasis on the
availability of proper consultancy and support in what can be
an extremely stressful and isolated role, and also on proper
administrative and secretarial support. Do the people in line
management understand what the staff are doing and what
constitutes good practice in this field? Are staff fully involved in
external decision-making processes which affect the home, and in
assessment and admission procedures? Above all, is the home
adequately staffed to provide care at the level suggested in this
chapter?

How other professionals perceive dementia sufferers
Finally, 'image' is reflected in access to other services. Elderly
people, whatever their mental health, are likely to need the
services of various medical specialists, dentists, opticians, solici-
tors, ministers of religion and other professionals. It may,
however, be difficult for dementia sufferers to make their needs
known, or, if known, to get them taken seriously even by staff.
And even when the need is recognised, the professionals' image
of a demented person together with difficulties in communication
and dread of a 'blocked' bed, can make it very difficult for the
staff to get the service which would be available to a younger or
mentally able person. We cannot say that residents in specialist
homes are being regarded and treated as true equals unless they
have equal access to services of all kinds.

Day care and respite care
Several of the establishments provide day care on their own
premises but on a varied basis. Some simply merge day care
attenders with residents and see the service as a flexible means
of providing support for carers (Vernon House, Dove House,
Williamwood House, Woodside). Bemerton Lodge is more
structured in its approach and employs an extra member of staff
for the purpose, but still provides integrated care. Bole Hill View

for social activities in the evening and at weekends. Flat Two is on the ground floor and differs from the other units in that a storeroom has been converted into a kitchen and the original kitchen made into a dining room to provide extra space. Also a Parker bathroom has been built on at one end. This is also used by other residents, since the home has only three other bathrooms including the one intended for day centre use. These alterations, which were made in 1981, cost £33,000.

The accommodation lies on each side of a passage which does a right-angle turn half way down, thus considerably lessening the institutional effect of a long, straight corridor, but everyone interviewed complained that the unit was too 'cramped and claustrophobic' to accommodate restless demented residents satisfactorily. At the time of the visit, however, they were all so physically disabled that this was not apparent. Access to the rest of the home is unrestricted, but a further door leading into the grounds is controlled by double handles which some residents can manage with ease. The OIC is seeking to have this linked to the internal alarm bell system so that they know if someone has gone out that way. There is also access to an enclosed paved garden which is being made as attractive as possible, but since the ground has been filled with rubble it is not possible to grass the area. Extensive grounds lie beyond, but these are open to the busy main road and considerations of road safety have prevented the authority from fencing them in.

The bedrooms have been made unusually homely compared with other SSD establishments included in this study. Most residents have photographs and ornaments, all have individual bedspreads and curtains, some have items of their own furniture, and the bareness of the plastic flooring is relieved by washable mats. Perhaps because of their accessibility and familiar furnishing, the bedrooms seem to be used much more by residents than is usual, and no attempt is made by staff to restrict this use, even though one resident used regularly to barricade herself in (see below). The Flat is bright with pictures and each resident's room is identified with a picture as well as with her name. Lack of space is particularly noticeable in the sitting room where there is scarcely room to move when all the residents are present, but attempts have been made to 'domesticate' it as far possible, and there is a pleasant, cluttered atmosphere. Two WCs are provided in the Flat and also a shower, but this has been turned into a junk room.

Ability range of residents

The level of both mental and physical disability is high with an average CRBRS score of 7.8. Four residents score 10 or 11. The other four are lower (4, 5, 6 and 7) but one of the most able has a longstanding paranoid illness. (This is the one who barricaded herself into her bedroom. She has now become secure enough to refrain from doing this.) Another constantly shouts 'where are you?' in order to gain attention and can become very agitated and difficult if she does not succeed, and one, though relatively mentally able, has almost no ability to communicate because of total deafness. One resident was bed-bound and thought to be dying at the time of the visit, two needed to be fed, one needed some assistance with feeding and only one was mobile without help.

Philosophy

Cambridgeshire SSD's definition of those who are suitable for residential care is unusually liberal. It will accept people who need help with dressing, toiletting and feeding and who are only mobile in a wheelchair, and any level of confusion, no matter how severe, 'so long as this does not present a management problem within the home in terms of aggression towards staff or disruption of the home life of more alert residents'. However, certain behaviour, 'eg regurgitation of food or indiscriminate toilet habits may indicate that a person is not suitable for admission'. Some degree of incontinence is not a bar to admission. A more detailed memorandum spells out criteria for admission to specialist units as follows:

'Placement will depend on the ability of the staff of the home to manage certain kinds of behaviour, but clients will normally be considered appropriately placed in a unit for those with special needs if they:

1. suffer from memory loss, and have lost insight into this, are disorientated about time and place, and are prone to wandering; and

2. are incapable of constructive thinking and have no appreciation of their condition; or

3. are incontinent, have deteriorated in their personal habits, and exhibit behaviour which is upsetting and unacceptable to other residents, thereby causing intolerance or agression among them, which cannot be managed by staff in the usual

Part III setting. Clients will normally be reasonably mobile. Aggression will not normally be tolerated, and extreme disruptive behaviour beyond the capability of the staff to manage may indicate the need for medical or hospital treatment. Clients who are generally frail, anti-social, or mentally ill may not be considered suitable on these grounds alone.

Clients will normally have been seen by the local psychogeriatrician or attendant services, or other consultant with special interest in the psychiatry of old age, who will provide advice and support to the home staff and general practitioner in their care of residents.'

The general approach of staff in Orchard House as a whole has a strong emphasis on self help, sharing in daily living activities and toleration of risk. Residents are encouraged to prepare their own breakfast and supper at a time convenient to themselves if they wish to do so; keys are provided if requested, and half the residents were on holiday in a hotel in Hastings when the initial visit for this study was paid. A great deal of attention is paid to promoting an appropriate lifestyle for each resident via the key worker system (see below). As far as is practicable these principles are carried through into the care provided in Flat Two.

Staffing
Staffing levels
All care staff are appointed to work throughout the home, going in and out of the different flats as required, but Flat Two has now acquired two staff who, in effect, work full-time in the unit: one who spends most of her time there, and one who is there half-time. In addition, one domestic gives 18 hours a week to the Flat and is an essential member of the staff. This permits two care staff to be on duty during the morning, and one during the rest of the day. Some extra help is also provided by staff who are available before the day centre attenders arrive and during bathtime in the evening. No special staff are on duty at night, when the Flat is covered by the two people covering the whole home. Overall, daytime staffing works out at 15.2 hours per resident week, the second lowest in the study, in spite of the heavy dependency levels, and even this amount has only been squeezed out by using hours previously allocated to the shortstay unit and to a part-time gardener. The original extra allocation was 40 hours a week (eg five hours per week per resident over and above the basic 5.8 hours allowed for all residents). Other

care staff and senior staff can be called on in a crisis, but these levels mean that all residents are left on their own while staff take breaks, and Flat Two residents have to be put to bed at 8 pm at night (see below). The home does have access to a 'pool' system which enables it to draw on extra staff to cover sickness and holidays, but this can only be used up to its allocation. In the opinion of the GP, any unusual sickness amongst staff or residents, or serious illness in more than one resident, can cause major problems, especially if the situation lasts a week or more, and he considers Orchard House as a whole to be seriously under-staffed in relation to the level of disability with which it copes.

Staffing qualifications and training
The OIC at the time of the visit had RMN, SRN and CSS qualifications (she had just completed the CSS course). Her deputy, who is also her husband, had no formal training. The third in charge is SRN, and the fourth had almost completed the CSS course, failing in one subject. None of the care staff had formal qualifications, but there was exceptional emphasis on in-service training. The induction process included working with an experienced colleague to cover a checklist of duties, and during their first year all new staff are encouraged to attend a course one day a week over a two-month period in conjunction with two other homes in the area.

The syllabus of this course is given below:

Session I: Tour around Symond's House and introduction to the course; film *Over the hill* which looks at old age and attitudes to it; what is caring? what jobs do we feel safe/unsafe with?

Session II: Pre-admission; reasons for admission; what this means to the client; discussion on residents' needs; the effects of living in an institution.

Session III: Tour around Orchard House; film *Don't spit, Gladys or Confusion without chaos* discussion of film, and management of confusion; causes and management of incontinence.

Session IV: Tour around Etheldred House (specialist ESMI home); diversional activities; the art of problem-solving: ways to help.

Session V: Loss, dying, death and bereavement; lifting, use of hoists and equipment.

Session VI: Practical care; diets

Session VII: Teamwork, continuity, care plans, working priorities; working with the deaf

Session VIII: Evaluation, training findings; Where do we go from here? Open period to be used as the group decides.

(A visit to Fulbourn Psychiatric Hospital is also arranged.)

The last hour of each training day is used for general discussion, and at the end of the course the trainees are given an opportunity to question the three OICs together about differences in the ways in which they run the homes.

The psychologist, who works half-time for the SSD, also runs a monthly group meeting with the Orchard House staff. He sees this as providing an opportunity to think about issues which have come up and look at problems in terms of *whose* problem? (ie is it a problem for the staff? the resident concerned? other residents?) and *why* is it a problem? and to facilitate the sharing of ideas. This formal session with an external facilitator acting as catalyst gives an opportunity to sit down and work out a method of dealing with issues which then becomes an automatic part of basic practice. These sessions were at first confined to members of the Flat Two staff, but the development of the key worker system has now encouraged involvement by the other staff who can see their relevance to their own work.

Individual on-going training is provided for key workers by the four senior staff who conduct an hour's one-to-one supervision session every three weeks, and meet groups of key workers every six weeks. Senior staff in turn have a supervision session with the OIC every two weeks. Holidays and sickness make it difficult to keep the system going as regularly as had been hoped, but the emphasis on the continuous review of progress and problems and the opportunity to discuss personal difficulties, is considered to be a key aspect of maintaining both staff morale and quality of care. In addition to the supervision sessions, meetings of domestic and of night staff are held every three months, and of care staff every four to six weeks. At senior level there is a strong local CSS course in which senior staff are strongly encouraged to take part, and there is consistent support from middle-management.

Staff communication

Basic information about all residents and the goals in their care plan are transcribed into a home-made 'Kardex' so that new staff, or those unfamiliar with short-term residents, can quickly grasp salient details of the people they are looking after. In Flat Two a detailed running record of events is kept with particular emphasis on any information which will improve communication with or understanding of residents. 'Handover' is simply a matter of reading the report book when coming on duty.

Regime

Getting up and going to bed

Night staff get two residents up as a matter of routine before they go off duty at 7.30 am, and the rest are usually up and dressed by 8.30 am (though people are allowed to lie in if they want to). One resident, who had had a tiring time the day before and was reluctant to get up, was still in bed at 11 am on the day of the visit. Because all Flat Two staff have gone off duty by 8.30 pm, residents have to be got to bed before then, and on the day of the visit one resident was lied to about the time to persuade her that it was bedtime.

Meals

Breakfast and supper are prepared and served from the Flat kitchen allowing maximum flexibility regarding individual preferences, and breakfast can be served as soon as someone is ready for it. The midday meal is brought up in hot lockers and dished out in the kitchen. It used to be served from dishes on the table, but this is no longer possible because of deterioration amongst the residents. Meals may be taken in the resident's own room or in the sitting room if this is preferred. The atmosphere is relaxed—for example one resident who uses her fingers to feed herself is given an apron and allowed to do so regardless of the mess. The dining room is very small (comparable in size to that in Highland House, see page 210) so there is not much room for segregation according to eating skills or table manners, but there is careful staff supervision of individual needs and knowledge of individual tastes. Sherry or wine is served in the evening as a 'night cap'.

Activities

There is no formal RO, but strong emphasis is put on one-to-one communication using knowledge of past experience and interests.

This knowledge is promoted by the information in the care plan and by the record book kept in the Flat in which information obtained from conversations is passed on. However, a unique aid to understanding and communication which ought to be widely imitated is to be found in personal 'history books' (on the lines of those used in children's homes) which record and illustrate the residents' lives using family snaps, pictures of past environments (librarians have proved very obliging in supplying early photographs of their towns), family trees, mementos of the war, illustrations relating to past employment, and written information obtained from the resident or relatives. Compiling these 'histories' is time-consuming and only two had been completed at the time of the visit, but the trouble is well worthwhile since they are invaluable in enabling staff to see the residents concerned as 'real people' and in relating present activities and events to past memories. A snapshot of a staff member's dog, for example, can be used to remind a resident of a pet illustrated in the 'history', or news about the miners' strike to a husband's occupation as a young man in Wales.

Imaginative use is also made of other aids to communication. For example, a set of glossy photographs published for primary school children and illustrating various traditional trades is effective in encouraging reminiscence. Self help is promoted as consistently as possible with the help of the care plan and residents are encouraged to take part in domestic activity. One chairbound person, for example, had some plates brought to her so that she could help dry up.

A lot of music is used with tapes of familiar songs and tunes, but television is not left on constantly. During the visit on a sunny summer afternoon, everyone who wished (one person refused) was wheeled or walked into the garden and were joined there by some residents from the other part of the home. In general, however, there is little interaction between Flat Two and the rest of Orchard House, although some attend a weekly singsong held in the evening in the day centre room (this is led by volunteers).

Clothing
The appearance of all the residents is attractive and dignified. Clothing may be bought on a shopping expedition with the key worker, or bought by the worker on the resident's behalf, or by relatives.

Bathing
Baths are normally given weekly and bed baths are given as required. Timing is according to preference, but the pattern is kept stable for each resident. An extra part-time member of staff is available to help with bathing in the evenings.

Management of continence
By day: Staff have a detailed knowledge of individual habits and take residents to the WC, or remind them to go, according to need. Maintaining continence is not felt to be much of a problem. Incontinence pads are used on outings, but not otherwise.

By night: Flat Two is unique in this study in that no special staff are assigned to this duty, and the two night staff cover the whole home. Residents are checked hourly unless this is likely to disturb them, 'the main point is that they should have a good night's sleep'. If they are found to be dead in the morning, 'that is a good way to go'. There is only one toilet round at 2 am and then 'only for those who are likely to need it'. A supply of Kylie sheets was being used up, but these will not be replaced as, unless they are carefully washed, they go hard and increase liability to bed sores. It is considered preferable to wash residents and change sheets as required.

Key worker system and use of a care plan
This system derives from the special project undertaken by the OIC when on her CSS course. She started from observing that those residents who respond and are easy to talk to get the most attention, while those who are already withdrawn are ignored, and that it is impossible for all members of staff to be aware of the special needs of every individual. Further, staff members cannot make effective use of short breaks in the routine provision of physical care if they are trying to 'socialise with everyone in half an hour'. They tend, therefore, to opt out of trying to make social contact and spend the time available talking to each other, or in the staff room 'writing the report'. To overcome these tendencies she has given staff members responsibility for relating to up to four residents—including knowledge of their tastes and history, contact with their family, and maintenance of their care plan, but not physical care. The role is seen as constituting increased responsibility for more experienced staff, and new staff are not immediately appointed as key workers. As was noted above, the system is closely linked to individual supervision sessions and also to use of the care plan which is drawn up in consultation with the resident and relatives. The first two pages

of the plan cover background information. This includes: what the person likes to be called; circumstances prior to admission (where? who with? what was it like?); reasons for admission; how the person reacted to admission; background and previous occupation; how the person occupied their time (including hobbies and interests); what kind of person he/she is (character, personality); what kind of things are impotant to him/her (beliefs, values etc); important contacts with the community; religion and church attended; particular likes and dislikes and usual habits relating to food and drink; usual bedtime, rising time, night-time waking/wandering and nap habits; and any other relevant information.

There follows a 'goal chart' which first asks: what does the person want for him/herself? what is the attitude of relatives/relevant others? what are the assets/abilities/strengths of the person? and then goes on to ask the key worker to tick boxes which refer to areas/needs/problems of concern and areas where further discussion is needed.

These are listed as follows:
- Mobility—walking; getting in/out of bed; stairs
- Eating
- Self care—washing; shaving; hair care; bathing
- Dressing
- Toiletting
- Sleep
- Sensory—sight; hearing
- Physical health
- General behaviour—restlessness; wandering; aggression; disruptiveness; noise; sexual; table manners; attention seeking
- Social—communication; socialising/mixing; participation in activities
- Psychological—memory; mood; self-esteem/identity; orientation; concentration

The most important areas to be identified are rated from 0 to 3 in terms of (1) desirability of change, (2) feasibility of change and (3) who needs to change (ie staff only, other residents only, the person concerned or a combination of the three). The areas with the highest totals are then broken down in terms of: what need of the individual the problem might reflect; exactly what the problem is; what happens leading up to/just before the problem; what happens as a result/following the problem; how often the problem occurs/when/how severe; any inconsistencies in whether the problem ocurs or not; when the problem does not occur.

When the problem area has been defined, the objective and the care plan are set out.

Originally it was not thought that this system (which in general is working well) would be needed in Flat Two because the staff based there already knew the residents so well. However, it transpired that one very involved worker was, in effect, acting as key worker for all the residents, and other staff were being excluded from this level of responsibility. The system is therefore being fully applied in Flat Two, and the senior officer with principal responsibility for the Flat (the fourth in-charge) also takes responsibility for individual supervision of the key workers concerned.

Personal allowance
One pound from the personal allowance is pooled and spent on items such as the nightly sherry, fresh fruit and pub lunches.

Outings
All the residents in Flat Two who wish to go are taken on a two-hour minibus ride with a pub lunch once a week. This is much enjoyed and there is no difficulty about acceptability at the pubs (as was noted above, incontinence pads are worn on these occasions). Occasional outings to zoos, country houses and so on are also undertaken when staff levels permit, but support is needed on a one-to-one basis.

Involvement with relatives
Using the care plan and building up the personal history books necessitate close involvement with relatives, as does the key worker system in general. Staff members sometimes accompany a resident on a visit to her family or on some other outing with relatives. There is no relative support group or other formalised system of contact.

Day care and respite care
Because of its volunteer management, the day centre is not able to cope with severe mental disability, but Flat Two is occasionally used to provide emergency day care. The shortstay beds provided in one flat in the home are not suitable for mentally-disabled people because staff cover is minimal, but it is hoped to develop Orchard House as a local resource centre and to use care staff

to provide care in people's own homes if a crisis occurs. It is also hoped to employ former staff members and other suitable people to provide a sitting-in service using money squeezed out of the day centre allocation.

Assessment and admission procedures

Each SSD team has set up its own arrangements for the allocation of beds on an area basis, and in Sawston this has developed into a multi-disciplinary group which meets at Orchard House and includes a district nurse, health visitor, GP and the representatives of voluntary bodies and the housing department, as well as social services personnel and the OIC. The group concentrates on identifying problems early and devising means to cope with them; longstay residential care is regarded as a last resort. However, Flat Two serves a wider area than that covered by this group and decisions concerning admission to the Flat are made by a sub-committee on the basis of agreed urgency and suitability (see page 106 for the SSD definition of appropriate clients). No waiting list is maintained.

An exceptionally detailed application/assessment/admission form for adult residential care is completed for all applicants. At Orchard House a key worker is allocated before admission and is responsible for visiting the prospective resident at home, meeting relatives, making detailed arrangements for admission and welcoming the new resident.

Professional support services
Psychiatrist
Fulbourn Psychiatric Hospital is an enormous institution with a vast catchment area, though it is only a few miles from Orchard House. Its 140 longstay psychogeriatric beds have to meet demand from the former counties of Cambridge and Huntingdon, a substantial part of Peterborough and a wedge of country on the Hertfordshire/Essex borders. Any specialist social services provision is therefore very much welcomed, though the consultant psychogeriatrician, Dr Peter Brooks, does not think that it is suitable for people suffering from very severe behaviour disorders such as faecal smearing, serious aggression, persistent agitation and restlessness and persistent absconding. He is much impressed by the ability and confidence of the OIC at Orchard House and has ceased to provide regular supportive visiting because he does not feel it is needed. He is, however, very willing to visit if asked to do so. In general he does not think that EMI units require very different facilities from ordinary residential care 'but what they

do need is more space and more staff'. Dr Brooks offers an assessment service for all potential residents in specialist units and use of this is standard practice.

Psychologist
Orchard House is unique in this study in having regular access to the services of a psychologist. Andrew Norris is based at Fulbourn, but his appointment is joint-funded between health and social services and he spends much of his time advising, supporting and training the staff of local authority homes in the management of mental disability. The value of this service has already been described. He is in favour of specialist wings, provided they have a distinctive ethos of close contact with and commitment to their residents, the staff are adequately trained and supported, and the objectives are clearly thought through. However, he thinks that the criteria for specialist care need to be more fully thought out. At present people tend to be referred for EMI provision simply because they have not fitted into ordinary homes—'decision by exclusion'—and there is no clear distinction between those who are suitable for specialist wings and those who need hospital care. There is also a tendency to consider all EMI as a homogeneous group when their needs may be very varied. Some require access to an enclosed garden; some need space for wandering inside the unit; some need to be contained; some are physically very frail; some need facilities specifically designed for coping with behavioural disorders and so on. However, the key factor is the personality, training and attitude of the OIC concerned.

General practitioner
Sawston contains the first health centre to be attached to one GP practice, and it has never lost the advantages in prestige and staffing which this guinea-pig status gave it. The village is also exceptionally well integrated as a community (in spite of a population which has trebled in recent years) and there is a strong tradition of voluntary activity and neighbourly support. The GP is very appreciative of the service which the home provides and sees it as his role to be particularly supportive to staff in times of crisis, or in the absence of the OIC. He is a member of the multi-disciplinary group which meets in Orchard House and is involved in the plans to extend the use of the home as a community resource. He is, however, critical of Flat Two as being too dark and claustrophobic and feels that the home's staff levels are too low to cope with any exceptional sickness in staff or

residents. He is also critical of the lack of provision in the area for EMI residents who become physically ill and who are not welcome in either the psychiatric or the geriatric hospital wards. It is clear that this GP's accessibility and support is of great importance to Orchard House.

District nursing service
Unlike many of the units described in this study, the district nurses are regularly involved in providing nursing care to residents in Orchard House. Although three residents in Flat Two are on their routine list they have no particular problems in treating them and would like to see more homes accept difficult residents. Many of their patients desperately need residential care, but cannot get places because they are too disabled, and this puts far greater strain on the district nursing service than the provision of a service to a place like Orchard House.

Summary
Flat Two is remarkable for its combination of high quality care with a severe level of physical and mental disability in its residents and a low staff level. Factors in this achievement include the triple training and personal qualities of the OIC, and the real interest, concern and dedication of the staff members who are particularly involved with the unit and who are very proud of what they have achieved. Like the special care unit at Bemerton Lodge, Flat Two has developed an ethos which is envied rather than disparaged.

Through good training, the use of the key worker system and regular individual staff supervision, the home as a whole has an atmosphere which is sympathetic to the provision of sensitive flexible care for *all* residents and Flat Two is therefore not seen as being basically different from the other units. The involvement of a psychologist with a real interest in this field of work is also a considerable advantage. No-one sees the physical design of the Flat as ideal for a specialist wing, and the OIC would like to build a new specialist unit in the grounds and allow Flat Two to revert to its original use for ordinary group living. The area of major concern, however, is a low level of staffing which results in residents being left unsupervised for long periods by both day and night, and means that the home as a whole survives on the edge of crisis. If Cambridge SSD is to continue to operate its admirably open policy with regard to the acceptance of very disabled applicants for residential care, it really must provide adequate staff levels.

BOLE HILL VIEW
Eastfield Road, Sheffield 10: Tel–0742 683 960

Principal characteristics
Bole Hill View is a purpose-built, local authority specialist home which combines 25 longstay beds, five shortstay respite/emergency places and a 20-place day centre, with the objective of offering a continuum of support throughout the period of dependency. The 'philosophy' is strongly oriented towards individualised care, using distraction and collusion rather than confrontation in the management of difficult or deluded behaviour, and with a high tolerance of 'calculated risk'. However, severe constraints are imposed on the regime by the design of the building and the combination of different forms of care in a relatively large institution.

History
Bole Hill View was opened in March 1983 as the fourth specialist home in Sheffield. Each home has its own characteristics and a comparative study would throw a good deal of light on the influence of design, personality and 'philosophy' in determining the way in which specialist care is provided, even within one authority. Sonia Sais, the OIC, who was largely responsible for the way in which Bole Hill View developed, left while this study was being written and it will be of interest to see whether and in what way the regime changes under her successor.

Design and furnishing
The home is built on the 'race track model' with rooms opening off a corridor running round a central enclosed courtyard. The passage originally ran through the very large dining room and lounge, with no dividing wall, making them in effect a part of the passageway. However, the lounge is now separate, and is subdivided by decorative partitioning. Two sides of the square are devoted to bedrooms (26 single and two double). A general staff office (originally intended as a further communal room), the day centre, and the laundry and staff accommodation respectively occupy the corners of the square. Six WCs are provided close to the lounge, but these have to be shared with day attenders. The remaining WCs are in the bedroom areas and there are no facilities close to the dining room or the entrance. There were only two bathrooms in the original design, but a third has now

been squeezed into the room also used for hairdressing and is primarily used for the day centre attenders.

The design has a number of drawbacks. The 'race track' model, while giving freedom to 'wander', encourages a compulsive non-stop perambulation which can lead to sheer physical exhaustion. The location of the bedrooms makes daytime staff supervision impossible, so their doors are secured by high bolts and they are not available to residents during the day. The original design also gave no separate access to the day centre, which limited its use by other community groups and produced a sense of 'invasion' when the day centre bus arrived. This has now been remedied, but the lack of lavatory accommodation means that day centre members still have to be brought down the lounge area on arrival and when they leave, so the situation is not much improved.

The office, which is centrally placed close to the front door, is the hub of activity with patients as well as staff constantly in and out. It is, however, too small for this purpose; a much larger office (see pages 155 and 243) encourages participation and minimises boundaries without inhibiting administrative and professional procedures. Staff sitting, changing and sleeping accommodation is still very inadequate, and was even more so in the original design. The staff bedroom has now been enlarged by taking over a resident's bedroom. The dining room is twice as big as is needed, and its use as a passage, along with a steeply-pitched V-shaped roof supported by a row of central pillars, further reduce any sense of domesticity. The passages have a very clinical look with strip lights, blank walls and uniform brown wooden doors, though these are well marked with residents' names (when the labels have not been torn off). Bedrooms are minimally furnished with a bed, chest of drawers, hanging cupboard and hand basin, but staff have done their best to 'personalise' them with wallpaper, matching curtains and bed covers. Some have personal ornaments and pictures, but only one small mat was observed. There is vinyl flooring throughout, except in the lounges and at points where the circular passage passes French windows opening onto the inner courtyard. These points have been provided with seating and are designed as informal sitting areas. Most staff dissatisfaction with design is focused on the lounge. Although this has now been subdivided, there are no barriers to sound, and the subdivision limits the possibility of creating small-scale groupings around occasional tables.

The feature about which staff are most enthusiastic is the laundry which is said to be the only item about which they were consulted.

Thus although the building is noticeably more spacious and more welcoming than older 'race track' homes, and a great deal has clearly been spent on it, it is still unsatisfactory in many ways. Its drawbacks illustrate the difficulty of designing a specialist home of this size which is not subdivided into smaller living units.

Ability range of residents
The CRBRS score shows a uniform level of severe disability which is only matched in this study by those being cared for in a hospital setting. The average is 9.4 with no less than 17 out of the 25 longstay residents at 10 or 11 and only three at 5 or 6—and these manifest severe behaviour disorders. The level of mobility is high, however, with only one really disabled resident. This may reflect a policy of encouraging walking (even at some risk) and the amount of perambulation encouraged by the 'race track' design, but it also reflects the deliberate use of the home to provide for people who are physically well but mentally very disabled, since it is this group who create most problems elsewhere and require particularly skilled management. (Indeed the selection panel rejects those who are not fully ambulent.) A surprisingly high proportion of the residents seem to have retained their ability to feed themselves compared with those of similar CRBRS scores elsewhere. This is attributed by the OIC to encouragement to go on eating independently even if they are messy eaters, use their fingers or take a long time to finish a meal.

Philosophy
Criteria for admission for longstay care is 'persons suffering from an irreversible form of cerebral degeneration whose mental state renders them incapable of independent living and whose behaviour has a deleterious effect on the life of others'. The staff do not see it as their role to cope with chronically physically ill people or with uncontrollable violence, but are prepared to manage almost any other form of behaviour. The emphasis is on fitting a minimal routine to residents' individual needs. 'We are resident-oriented, not task-oriented.' The system encourages one-to-one relationships and activities between staff and residents, both inside and outside the home, and minimises aggression and frustration by avoiding confrontation and colluding with delusional ideas if necessary. There is constant effort to understand where a resident's mind has taken him and to be

there with him. The policy of 'calculated risk management' entails making no attempt to restrain those at risk of falling and the unlocked front door demands acceptance of occasional wanderings to remote parts of the city. Experience has shown that residents who undertake such journeys are in fact capable of crossing roads safely and the main physical harm incurred has been from severe sunburn! The corollary of this relaxed and individualist style of care is the need to put maximum reliance on individual staff members' judgement and capacity for accepting responsibility in use of time and mode of delivering care.

Staffing
Staff levels
It is not easy to calculate staff levels for the longstay residents separately as the staff group as a whole also services the 20-place day centre and the five shortstay beds. The senior staff not only manage all three sectors, but also undertake home visits to day centre attenders and potential residents. The home is, however, staffed at double the usual Sheffield level with 1,096 care assistant hours per week, including night care which is covered by all staff on a rotating basis. In addition, a craft instructor is employed mainly in the day centre, and there is the usual Sheffield provision of four senior staff for a home of this size. If assumed hours for night care, the day centre and all senior staff time are deducted, the average per resident week (including the short-term residents) works out at about 26.8 hours—the most generous local authority ratio in the study. In addition there are 240 domestic hours (including laundry) and 56 cooking hours, and there is a strong emphasis on blurring roles between domestic and care staff. In all, 52 staff are on the books. It must be noted, however, that in the view of the OIC this level of staffing is required because of the combination of physical mobility and severe mental impairment. If people who were immobile or nearly so were accepted and retained, they could manage with fewer staff. It should also be noted that the time of senior staff is very largely taken up with administrative work, plus 'outreach' to day centre clients and their families. No clerical officer or handyman is employed (though this would seem to be a most cost-effective use of resources) and the allocation of domestic staff is related to the number of residents rather than the size of the building. Good care staff are constantly being lost to nurse training or other careers and the OIC regrets that there is no clear ladder of training and promotion for care staff, with an intermediate 'senior care assistant' role as a halfway house to officer status.

Staff qualifications and training
At the time of the visit the OIC had both RMN and CQSW qualifications and her deputy was RMN/SRN, while the other senior staff had the CSS. Care staff were mostly without formal qualifications and had been selected on the basis of their motivation and flexibility. They tend to be young as the OIC believes that younger people are likely to have more initiative and energy and fewer pre-conceptions about the proper way to provide care. (Another informant, however, felt that older people coped better with very difficult residents.) She also likes to mix the sexes and there were five male care assistant staff employed at the time of the visit. After an initial one-week induction course, training is meant to be on the basis of a weekly one-to-one session with a senior member of staff, though this does not always happen. (No other unit visited had this level of personal supervision.) Care staff also have a booklet listing topics on which they are expected to receive training in the course of their work, and when and how this has been provided. Because all staff share night and day duty, day centre work and escort duty on the day centre bus, a wide variety of experience can be offered.

Staff communication
There is strong emphasis on the importance of communication; the senior staff see their principal role as caring for the care staff, thus enabling them to care for the residents. Apart from detailed handover sessions, senior staff meetings and general staff meetings (including domestics) are meant to be held fortnightly, though again this does not always happen. A day book is kept and the staff on duty in particular corridors also make notes on 'their' residents which are used for the handover session and are written up in summary form in the resident's notes once a week. First names are used by all staff and no uniforms are worn. The general atmosphere is exceptionally relaxed and there is a strong awareness in the senior staff of the need to support care assistants in what is felt to be a stressful environment.

Regime
Getting up and going to bed
There is no set getting-up time and most residents are dressed by day care staff when they wake up, breakfast being a staggered meal which may last till 10.30 am. However, it is recognised that some residents would 'sleep till dinner time' if they were not wakened and this is left to the judgement of the care staff

concerned. The dressing process is conducted in privacy in individual rooms with closed doors, and particular staff are allocated to each corridor to ensure that the work is fairly distributed and there is continuity in the encouragement of self help. The process of going to bed is similarly staggered depending on usual habits and apparent sleepiness, but residents would be allowed to sit up all night if they wished to do so.

Meals

Breakfast is served after the kitchen staff come on duty at around 7.30 to 7.45 am and consists of porridge or cornflakes, a plated cooked course, and bread or toast. Exercise of choice is encouraged. All residents wear plastic cooking aprons of various designs for the meal. Tables are set for four with 26 places laid, but the staggered timing means that residents can be helped individually as required. Lunch is served at 12 noon with a plated first course and choice of puddings. Those who need most help are seated on one side of the room. Tea, which is a light meal, was served at 4.30 pm in the lounge at the time of the visit because the dining room was being redecorated.

Activities

Apart from a small group of the most able residents who take part in daily living activities, there is little joint activity. Staff are encouraged to respond to residents on a one-to-one basis and, if they can be spared, key workers may take residents out by themselves to shop, visit a pub and so on. Once a week the day centre coach is available to take residents for a drive.

Bathing

As was noted above, the provision of baths is inadequate. Bathing is managed by the 'corridor staff' on the basis of individual preference and need and the availability of time.

Management of continence

By day: Continence is successfully maintained by regular toiletting and observation of individual patterns of need. Pads and catheters are not used. There is very little smell. Staff give enemas as required.

By night: Kylie sheets are used routinely as an alternative to disturbing sleep by toiletting rounds at night. Commodes are not used in bedrooms.

Reviews

The application for residential care, if properly completed, gives an exceptional amount of information about the resident who is in any case likely to be well known to staff through day care and respite care before being accepted for long-term admission (see below). Six weeks after admission a review is held at which the senior field social worker and two or three care staff, including the key worker, are present, but this is felt to be a formality because the only alternative placement at that stage would be long-term hospital care. Each resident has a key worker who is responsible for maintaining contact with the family, supervising clothing and purchases, encouraging individual activity, and generally befriending. Progress or problems are discussed with a senior officer at the weekly supervision sessions. An immediate meeting of relevant staff may be called at any time to discuss a particular crisis in care provision and management.

Personal allowance

This is held centrally and claims are made against individual accounts for personal purchases and expenses.

Outings

As was noted above, there is a regular bus trip once a week and staff take residents out on a one-to-one basis as time allows.

Involvement with relatives

Contact with relatives is exceptionally close because of the relationship built up through the provision of day care and emergency/respite care, and through staff visits to homes when acting as escort on the day centre bus or to discuss care and management. When the patient is in long-term care this close contact is maintained through the use of a key worker and through a policy of encouraging relatives to continue to give personal care if they wish to do so. A lot of time is given to providing support, expressing understanding of relatives' feelings of exhaustion, guilt and anger, and working through pre-death mourning. A relatives' group is held fortnightly which is run by relatives themselves with a staff 'facilitator' (this group was originally set up by a CQSW student on placement). One relative whose mother has now died does most of the organisation for this and provides support between meetings. Relatives are also encouraged to come to parties and fund-raising events.

The following is part of a letter which had just been put on the notice-board at the time of the visit:

'To my dear friends
I would just like to thank you all for the love and care you gave to Mum. She died surrounded by love in the place she came to know as home. All of you helped when I needed help most, something that I will not forget. I have chosen these few words for you with all love and gratitude ...' (Then follows a quotation, thanking God 'for all good people'.)

Volunteers
Relatives may act as informal volunteers, for example by giving out night time drinks, but otherwise the work is felt to be too stressful for volunteer involvement. However, one volunteer does come regularly on one afternoon a week to help with clerical work, and this is greatly appreciated.

Day care and respite care
The staff see day care both as a service in its own right and as a means of providing a flexible, carer-oriented transition from independence to total care. In spite of this, the home and the centre operate as separate units and there is little contact between day attenders and residents, except for shared use of WCs and time spent in the lounge waiting to be collected by relatives. Some day attenders do, however, like to wander round the home and they are free to do so. One client, a former businessman, sees going out 'to the office' as a natural and acceptable procedure, whereas going to a day centre is not, so he spends all his time in the home's office. (It is the staff's matter-of-fact acceptance of quirks of this kind which is one of the strongest features in the way in which Bole Hill View operates.) The combination of day care, respite care and longstay care means that care can be offered as and when it is needed, including evenings and weekends, and the home prides itself on never refusing to meet real need. 'If we tell them they can rely on us, we have to prove that we mean it.' It also means that detailed knowledge of the home and family is built up so that if regular respite care or longstay care becomes necessary, there is no sense of sudden transition. However, the amount of social work involved in supporting the families of day care attenders does mean that the OIC has to give time from the needs of residents and staff which is difficult to spare. The tension between provision

for day care clients and the needs of very dependent longstay residents is again clearly demonstrated at Bole Hill View.

Five rooms, grouped together, are kept entirely for shortstay clients, whether for regular respite, holidays or emergencies. Users are usually day centre attenders and so are already well known and familiar with the home and staff—a familiarity which is promoted by the practice of not employing separate staff for the day centre. The availability of these beds is regarded as a key aspect of the home's role as a 'resource'. Difficulties sometimes arise because people in for shortstay are likely to be more able than longstay residents, but as they can use the day care facility during the day and have their own rooms at night, this is not often a serious problem. The long-term residents are not sufficiently aware of their neighbours to feel 'invaded'.

Assessment and admission procedures
The application form used by social services for admission to an EMI home is exceptional and includes:

● *Clinical evaluation*—which covers mental and physical condition, the nature and extent of disruptive or anti-social activity and the effects of this behaviour on primary carers and others.
● *Social work report*—which gives details of housing, domiciliary services received, next of kin and brief biographical account of past history. It covers such areas as social contacts, interests, activities and hobbies along with details of physical capabilities (for example the ability to climb stairs, or make a cup of tea). The applicant's ability to respond appropriately to others, to find his way around the house or neighbourhood, and recall recent or earlier events is also considered. Details of behavioural patterns, including those which are likely to cause discomfort or distress to others, are included.

Impressive as this form is in theory, in practice the Bole Hill staff often fill most of it in themselves because they know the prospective resident much better than the field social worker does.

All applications for admission to the four specialist homes are considered by an admission panel which meets fortnightly. This is chaired by the chief assistant—residential services (adults) and consists of the OICs of the four homes, nominees of the fieldwork social services division and members of the psycho-geriatric team (see below). In theory, the panel accepts medical as well as social services referrals, but in practice it has to decide between four people who have already been preselected as being at most risk in the community. People who have got into the 'medical pathway' are therefore likely to be admitted to NHS care unless a direct swop is arranged between someone who has proved unmanageable in a specialist home and someone in hospital who is considered suitable. Such a swop would not go through the admission panel. There is no requirement for hospital assessment before admission to Bole Hill View.

Professional support services
General practitioner
A very supportive GP visits weekly on a routine basis. He is on informal, first-name terms with staff and sees it as part of his role to reassure them and to relieve anxiety—especially when a resident is dying. He gives staff some discretion in drug administration—'There is no point in waking someone up to give him a sedative.' There is a mutual confidence between the GP and staff. He says he feels care staff know their residents and that he will not be called in inappropriately, and they are assured of his understanding of the regime and his availability whenever needed. Such a relationship seems to be essential in a home of this kind.

District nursing services
Staff carry out all necessary nursing procedures and the district nursing service is not involved.

Psychogeriatric service
The Northern General Hospital provides 25 acute/assessment psychogeriatric beds for patients with functional illness, and 24 longstay beds; Middlewood, which is a traditional hospital, provides another 100 longstay beds. These facilities are shared between two psychogeriatricians responsible for the northern part of the health district. One of these, Dr Wendy Bant, visits Bole Hill View monthly on a regular basis, to discuss residents who are giving concern and also to agree on support plans for patients who are still in the community and who may need day care and respite care. She is available at any time if required. The other (full-time) consultant has a team approach and works closely with social work, psychologist and CPN colleagues who are mainly in contact with Lytton House, another specialist home. They visit this monthly and sit on the admission panel which meets there. They feel that the specialist homes are functioning

well, but that they are not able to cope with active male residents. 'We don't propose them for admission because we know they would only be sent back to us.' In consequence, the NHS facilities have a high proportion of men—44 out of 130 longstay patients. As was noted above, there is a tendency for those who come to notice via medical rather than social services referral to stay in the hospital system if they need long-term care, but Middlewood Hospital is due to close in ten years, and consideration is being given to an alternative provision of longstay beds. The psychogeriatric team is strongly in favour of very small domestic units, but these may be too expensive to be practicable, and it is likely that services will develop on a cottage hospital model. However, it is felt that the Trent regional directive on staffing levels is unrealistic for very dependent longstay patients.

Social services
A senior field social worker, who can be consulted at any time, visits Bole Hill View every month to discuss clients who are receiving, or may need, day care and respite care with the OIC. It is clear that relationships on this level are excellent. However, there is little contact with the line manager in charge of residential homes, and what contact does exist is related to administrative matters, rather than quality of care, and the particular stresses of running a specialist home. The OIC feels strongly that understanding and support at management level are essential for the successful operation of specialist care and that 'EMI homes cannot exist in a vacuum'. She was very anxious that this lack of understanding may result in Bole Hill View being run in a much more traditional way after she left, and that the approach which she had tried to pioneer might be destroyed.

Summary
Bole Hill View demonstrates the value of combining longstay care with shortstay beds and day care, but also its costs in terms of an unwieldy size of premises and staff, a very heavy commitment to fieldwork by the senior staff and a consequent tendency (noted so frequently in this report) for time and energy to be drained away from the most dependent, longstay residents. It also demonstrates, yet again, the key importance of the 'philosophy' and personality of the OIC and the potential which untrained staff have to develop a high level of skill, commitment and responsibility. However, the Bole Hill View regime has not been achieved without a considerable level of personal stress, and there is no doubt that the higher the objectives in relating to severely

dependent people as individuals and maintaining personal contact with them, the greater the demands on the care staff at all levels. The nature of this stress and the ways in which staff can be helped to cope with it demands much more attention than it has so far received.

VERNON HOUSE
Turncroft Lane, Woodbank, Stockport:
Tel–Stockport 428 5361

Principal characteristics
Vernon House is a long-established 'race track' home which, at
the time of the visit, provided specialist care for 30 very severely
disabled people (including one shortstay bed) but this is now
reduced to 28. It has the lowest staffing level found in this report.
A new unit providing for six shortstay residents has recently been
added as a Demonstration Development District (DDD) project
(see page 138). The quality of care offered, though good when
related to the building, levels of dependency, and levels of staffing,
is not remarkable. However, the home has been included in the
study because it demonstrates the potential for change in
establishments which have previously been run on very traditional lines; because a number of issues are raised by the
addition of the DDD project; and because it operates in a health
district where there is an ESMI unit but no psychogeriatrician.
Stockport's plans for training care staff are also of considerable
interest. The home demonstrates very clearly that specialist SSD
care must always be considered in the context of other service
provision.

History
Vernon House was opened in 1968 as a Part III home under the
control of the Local Authority Health Department. It has
operated as one of the four specialist homes in the Borough since
1971. Before Barbara Munsch was appointed OIC in 1977 the
regime, by all accounts, justified the criticisms which have been
levelled at residential care in general and specialist care in
particular.

Some changes were introduced immediately by the new OIC and
others have come more gradually, as staff were replaced and
conditions of service could be altered. Delegation of responsibility
to senior staff for a particular area of care or administration, such
as catering or drug management, is a recent development arising
from the CSS course just completed by the OIC. Senior staff are
now also responsible for the supervision and training of a group
of care staff, and a modified key worker system is in operation.

131

Design and furnishing

The main building now provides five two-bedded and 18 single rooms on two sides of the central courtyard. The third side has a large lounge, which can be divided by a flexible partition, and a smaller room now used as a dining room for more able residents. The main entrance on the fourth side leads into a lobby furnished with about eight chairs which creates a popular place for sitting. The office is on one side of the lobby, and the main dining room and kitchen on the other. The central courtyard is grassed and has some quite large trees which add considerably to the attractiveness of the building. Residents have free access to it, but it is said to become extremely hot in summer. There is also an enclosed garden to one side of the home with access from one of the bedrooms, and quite extensive further grounds which border on a park. Nine WCs are provided in the main house arranged in one block of three and three blocks of two, and there are two bathrooms, one with a medi-bath. Although the home itself is single-storey, two staff flats are provided on the first floor. The front door can be opened from the outside, but egress is controlled by a key which is then 'posted' back through a letter-box into the staff room. Residents' rooms in the main house are kept locked during the day and there is no provision for privacy in the shared rooms. Few personal possessions are displayed, the staff saying that they have great difficulty in keeping such things where they belong, but there are pictures on the walls and the rooms have been individualised with wallpaper on one wall, curtains and bedspreads. Furniture and furnishings, however are minimal, and built-in fitments make it difficult for residents to bring in their own.

A wing has been built onto this basic plan providing a small lounge, six well-furnished single rooms, two WCs and a bathroom with a Parker bath. This was built in 1984 with money obtained under the 'Rising Tide' programme and is specifically intended for planned respite care. There are no separate dining facilities, so temporary residents have to come into the main home for meals and, in practice, any segregation has proved impossible so that longstay residents wander into the shortstay unit and vice versa.

Ability range of residents

With an average score of 8.6 on the CRBRS scale and a third of the residents scoring 10 or 11, Vernon House is certainly coping with levels of mental disability comparable to a longstay hospital ward. At the time of the visit three residents required total care and were probably dying, and at least six needed to be fed, while others required encouragement and assistance to continue eating. Almost all needed help in walking, or guiding to their destination. There is one Chinese resident who suffers from fairly severe dementia, but with whom verbal communication is impossible in any case because of the language barrier.

Philosophy

The OIC takes care not to admit anyone to the main home who would be distressed by the overall level of disability and at the time of the visit had, in fact, just insisted on the transfer of a lady admitted as an emergency who, though very deluded, was aware of her surroundings and distressed by them. Any type or level of behavioural disorder can be coped with except for uncontrollable aggression to other residents. Problems relating to a mix of abilities can, however, arise with the DDD clients who are admitted under a separate system. Residents are transferred to a geriatric ward if their physical condition demands specialist equipment or skilled nursing care, but most are cared for till death. There is no written statement on philosophy, but the general approach is: to personalise care as far as staffing levels allow; to observe very closely in the period after admission; to develop good relationships with relatives; to be aware of individual tastes; and to provide dignified personal clothing.

Staffing
Staff levels

Only ten hours a week of care staff time per resident is allowed—the lowest provision found in this study. Yet Stockport gives its specialist homes 25 per cent more staff than its ordinary homes and has, indeed, been criticised by the Audit Commission because its staffing levels were thought to be too generous by comparison with other metropolitan districts! The low level of staffing means that senior staff and domestics have to share in the provision of personal care, and it is estimated that the four senior staff use about a quarter of their time in this way; they also work a great deal of unofficial overtime. The staff/resident ratio is improved by 1.4 hours if the 120 care hours allowed under the DDD project are included in the calculation. Indeed the fact that the DDD unit is considered to require 20 hours per resident week is some indication of how severely under-provided the main home is. It also illustrates how much easier it is to obtain reasonable levels of staffing in new establishments than to build up levels in older ones.

A split shift system is operated, with a change-over at 5 pm while residents are having their tea, so that one lot of staff can start them off and another clear up, and the residents do not have to be hurried. Similarly, in the morning, one member of the care staff comes on duty at 7 am to help with the last hour of work before the night shift go off duty. Senior staff work a double shift combined with sleeping-in so that they come on duty at 2 pm, go off at 10 pm and work again from 8 am to 2 pm. On the day of the visit the member of staff concerned was, in fact, helping to hand round tea at 7 am.

Staff and training qualifications
The OIC has psychiatric nursing experience and has recently completed the CSS. None of the other staff at Vernon House have formal qualifications. In general, Stockport follows a policy of 'growing its own residential staff' by promoting those who have shown their quality as care assistants to work as deputies, with assessment for salary progression after one year. They are always transferred from the home where they worked at a more junior level.

Senior staff are encouraged to take the CSS course. All new care staff do a basic two-day course on attitudes, home nursing skills, first aid and so on, and they have an opportunity to attend one-day courses on specific subjects such as arthritis, incontinence, Parkinson's Disease and strokes. (A specialist incontinence adviser is available to all homes, though she does not seem to be much used at Vernon House.) Informal induction training with a schedule of topics to be covered is being planned at Vernon House. Staff can also apply to do a one-year, in-service course with weekly day release. All the senior staff at Vernon House have completed this course, as have three care assistants, and six more have applied to do it this year.

The major points of interest, however, are two 'rolling pro-grammes' of training which are about to get under way. One of these is aimed at care staff of *all* kinds including home helps, nursery assistants, social workers in children's homes, and staff in mental handicap and mental illness hostels, as well as sheltered housing wardens and care staff in old people's homes. It is hoped that eventually it will become possible to include NHS staff. The

134

course, which is being provided in association with Stockport College of Technology, will teach people in multi-disciplinary groups of 25 and start with a five-day block followed by completion of a specific project in the work situation, and a further three-day block two weeks later. The aim is to eradicate myths about the nature of each other's jobs, change attitudes to the task and client, and encourage relating what is learned back to the work situation. A second phase of training will cover specialist areas of interest. Plans for the course are currently being worked through with senior management, trades unions and OICs.

Even more important perhaps is a parallel inter-disciplinary training course aimed at management staff. The training officer takes the view that it is useless to train at shop floor level if managers do not understand the attitudes and concepts which are being taught, and continue to regard the provision of care as an unskilled physical task: 'To be effective, training needs to start with the SSD Director.' Therefore, over the next two years it is proposed that *all* senior SSD staff up to assistant director level (they evidently chickened out of including the director) will join in seven groups of 20. These will be in one three-day block with a follow-up day later on, and will have a strong emphasis on techniques of staff supervision, training and support. Specialist professional help is being brought in to run these courses. It is to be hoped that these training experiments will be used as pilots for similar developments all over the country, since it has been evident again and again in preparing this report that it is of little use having creative and dedicated individuals working in particular establishments if ancillary services and management are not provided with the same objectives and with the same quality of care.

Staff communication
A limited key worker system is in operation which gives care staff responsibility for observing and meeting the needs of particular residents, and maintaining contact with them and their families. A key worker may, for example, buy a present for a resident to give a family member on her birthday. Each senior staff member is responsible for a group of care staff and meets with them on a monthly basis to discuss 'their' residents and other aspects of care giving. The OIC has individual supervision sessions with senior staff. Handover sessions are limited to purely

practical issues and individual record-keeping is not extensive, but a detailed 'communications' book is kept.

Regime
Getting up and going to bed
As was noted above, a member of the day care staff comes on duty at 7 am to help night staff with the getting-up process, and the senior staff member who is sleeping in usually helps also. No one is woken up in order to get them up, but about a third of the residents were in fact dressed by 7.30 am on the day of the visit. Breakfast is available from 8.30 am and can be served at any time after that. In the evening, drinks are served around 7.30 or 8 pm and people are put to bed gradually after that time. On the day of the visit all but one resident was in bed by 10.30 pm, but several were up and wandering round the home during the night. Dressing and undressing is done in the bedrooms and external privacy is well maintained.

Meals
It was difficult to observe ordinary practice on the day of the visit because the small lounge, which is used as an extra dining room for more able residents, was being re-floored and everyone was crammed into the main dining room, except for two chairbound people who are always fed where they are sitting in the lounge. (This is usually done by the staff member who is also keeping an eye on the small dining room next door.) Meals are dished up on the kitchen hatch and staff showed good awareness of individual tastes. Care was taken, for example, to make sure that a new DDD resident who was in for the first time was not served pork or bacon which he disliked because 'it is forbidden in the Bible'. Efforts are sometimes made to get a meal in from a take-away or to cook specially for the Chinese resident, but she frequently rejects this and wants to have the same as other residents. Fish and chips on Fridays is a popular dish. Breakfast is an uncooked meal to allow maximum flexibility, lunch is a two-course meal, and tea, served at 4.30 pm, is a cooked snack, except on Wednesdays when the cook leaves early and sandwiches are provided. A further supper snack is provided for those who want it at around 8.30 pm.

In addition to the two very disabled people left in the lounge, four residents need to be fed, and many need active help to eat and not to interfere with each other's food. At least two additional members of staff are needed for this, apart from those engaged in dishing up and clearing, and everyone on duty, including senior staff, is involved. Cutlery, glasses and water jugs are not put out until the meal is ready; otherwise they 'would be all over the place'. At weekends, 'afternoon tea' is provided in the lounge and shared by visiting relatives, residents and staff. This encourages elderly relatives to treat their visit as 'a day out', promotes informal contact with staff and makes it possible to visit without the strain of having to maintain prolonged one-to-one contact with a resident who cannot respond. A cooked snack is served later in the evening on these days.

Activities

Staffing levels do not permit any routine organised activity at present, though it is hoped that an OT aide, who is being provided by the DDD project, will also get things going in the main house. An attempt was made some time ago to run a small RO group with four of the most able residents, while sitting with them round a tea-table and drinking tea. This proved very successful, but it was impossible to keep it going because of pressure of work. Singsongs do develop on Saturday and Sunday evenings when there is no paper work to be done and senior staff have time to sit with residents. Parties and barbeques take place from time to time with the help of the relatives of both residents and staff, and volunteer entertainers give a performance from time to time in the winter months. Occasional outings take place—for example a trip on a canal barge—but this demands finding enough volunteers to provide one-to-one escorts.

Clothing

It took a great deal of persistence to establish the change from communal clothing to a genuinely and consistently individualised system, but this has now been achieved. One domestic works for the whole of every weekday morning in the laundry and she says that sorting clothing and putting it back in residents' rooms is a considerable part of the task. Clothing appears suitable and dignified.

Bathing

Baths are given in the evening, as far as possible by the responsible key worker. Staff make their own decisions about timing and need.

Management of continence

By day: Residents are taken to the WC as a matter of routine

before and after meals and at other times according to knowledge of individual habits. A bowel book is kept, but incontinence charts are not used. Incontinence pads are used if necessary, mainly for bowel incontinence. Enemas are avoided as far as possible, and when needed are given by the district nurse.

By night: Residents are disturbed as little as possible and kept comfortable by the use of Kylie sheets and incontinence pads. Commodes are provided in all bedrooms.

Reviews
After the initial assessment period (see below) there is no formal review, apart from discussion in the care assistant team meetings. There is no system of goal planning.

Personal allowance
This is used for individual needs at staff discretion, the remainder being banked by the local authority.

Outings
Group outings take place occasionally but one-to-one expeditions are mainly limited to essential visits to the oculist, dentist and so on. Again this is determined by shortage of staff and frailty of residents.

Involvement with relatives
There is no formal relatives' group attached to the main home, though efforts are being made to develop one in relation to the DDD project. Families are encouraged to visit at any time and the provision of Saturday and Sunday afternoon tea for them has already been noted. Relatives also help in the work involved in holding parties and fund-raising events. Staff are strongly oriented to trying to help relatives with their guilt about no longer providing care, and to put over the message 'if she is dependent enough to be admitted here, there is no way in which you could have coped at home'. Their success in 'not being critical of families' was commented on by the line manager.

Volunteers
The informal assistance given by both relatives and the families of staff has already been noted. Regular volunteer involvement is difficult to maintain because of the lack of response to personal contact from residents, but some volunteers have managed to 'stick'. One schoolgirl started coming when she was 13 and

continued until she went to college, and another helper came almost every evening over a long period. Roman Catholic and Anglican clergy hold services regularly.

Day care and respite care
Informal day care is provided by individual arrangement if the family can arrange transport and also as an introduction to the home before permanent admission, but this facility is not extensively used—indeed, there would be not enough space or staff to provide it on any scale. Under the DDD project, care between 10 am and 7 pm for eight people a day on seven days a week is given in a purpose-built annexe attached to another specialist home which is a considerable distance away.

One shortstay bed is kept free in the main home for relief and emergency admission and for trial stays. This is under the control of the OIC who uses it to provide a service which is as informal and flexible as possible. The six respite beds in the DDD unit were very poorly taken up at the time of the visit. This was attributed to the complex assessment and admission procedures demanded by the experimental nature of the project; lack of awareness about the facility amongst the general public; strict application of a rule that the facility is to be used by those who are not already receiving help; lack of allowance in the project budget for senior staff administration; and the separation of the day care and respite care facilities.

Assessment of the DDD project is not a proper part of this study, but the point does need to be made that an annexe of this kind cannot be built onto an established home without very careful consideration of: the compatibility of the two sets of residents if mixing is encouraged or unavoidable; the roles of all the staff concerned; administrative and social work responsibility for the respite patients; and the additional strain on the resources of the home. The proper relationship between respite care, day care and longstay care also needs consideration. As Bole Hill View (page 118) and Dove House (page 164) illustrate, there are major advantages in providing all three on the same site and encouraging gradual movement from one form of care to another, but there are corresponding dangers in drawing off staff to look after the most rewarding and least disabled clients. The DDD annexe at Vernon House certainly illustrates the danger of giving one-off grants to authorities to set up showy new services, rather than assisting them to make basic improvements in the quality of service provision.

Assessment and admission procedures
Referrals go to the senior social worker in a domiciliary care
team which specialises in the care of elderly and physically
handicapped people. (Each specialist home serves a catchment
area covered by two such teams.) Excellent physical assessment
of applicants is available on a routine basis by arrangement with
the geriatrician. Psychiatric assessment can be obtained by
requesting a domiciliary visit or admission to the ESMI unit as
an in-patient or day patient, but lack of a psychogeriatric
specialist limits the usefulness of the information obtained. The
referral may come from the local ESMI unit, the geriatric hospital,
another old people's home or direct from the community, but in
practice, considerations of social need almost always favour
people still living in the community as against those in any kind
of institution. When the social worker, in consultation with the
OIC of Vernon House, has decided who should be offered a
vacant bed, a senior officer from the home and the care assistant
who will act as key worker visit the client and her relatives and
arrange for her to come for a 'trial' day. During this day the
likelihood of the proposed resident 'settling', the level of disability, and any management problems are assessed. The trial day
may be omitted if the client is already well known to the home.
The trial continues during the first six weeks of admission and
during this period detailed notes are kept by all staff concerned
with the resident. The key worker summarises the information
obtained during this period onto an assessment form.

At the end of the six week trial the information thus collected is
considered at an assessment meeting chaired by the senior social
worker from the specialist team. This meeting is also attended
by the OIC, the social worker or social services officer who had
previously been in contact with the client, and the residential
services officer; relatives are also invited. The process is particularly important in ascertaining who is not disabled enough, or
who is too disturbed, for Vernon House and the assessment
meeting is treated as a serious part of the admission process,
although, of course, finding a suitable alternative may be
extremely difficult.

Professional support services
Psychiatric services
The DGH, which is called Stepping Hill, includes a purpose-built
ESMI unit of the standard north western region type (for a
description of this, see York House, page 186). It was opened in

1979 and, like York House, it provides 28 shortstay respite and assessment beds, 28 longstay beds for dementia sufferers and a 30-place day hospital. There are, however, major difficulties both in making full use of the unit and integrating it with the four specialist SSD homes and other community-based services. As a result, the day hospital has only 18–20 patients coming in daily, and in June 1985 only six of the eight beds reserved for assessment were used. The causes of this situation are complex. The core of the problem seems to be that there is no psychogeriatrician with overall responsibility for integrating and developing service provision. One senior registrar does devote two sessions to the unit, mainly in relation to assessment, and she is willing to visit EMI homes on request, but the rest of her time is taken up with adult and child psychiatry. The five psychiatric consultants based at Stepping Hill are reluctant to divide their work on a geographical basis because it would mean that most of their patients would be of a similar type and social class. They therefore take referrals from any GP who happens to know them, or because they are on duty when a call comes in, and they accept adult patients of any age. If their patients are admitted to the ESMI unit, they follow them up there so there is no unified ward round. The situation is further complicated by the fact that the Stockport Health Authority also covers North Derbyshire. This demands liaison with another social services department which has no specialist homes and which does not provide a social worker to liaise with the ESMI unit. At the time of the visit, there was one CPN and one social worker (only recently in post) based in the unit, and both were working to all six doctors. Plans were being made for the appointment of two more CPNs and four specialist social workers to be based in the ESMI unit and to have responsibility for liaising with the four area teams and EMI homes, but some informants expressed reservations about the plan because it might be divisive to allocate workers to clients on the basis of a diagnostic label. There would also be problems in liaison between social workers who had a geographically-based field of responsibility, and psychiatrists who did not.

An attempt has been made to improve communication between the unit and SSD staff by setting up fortnightly 'community' meetings. These are attended by senior medical staff, ward and community-based nurses, an OT and the social worker from the unit, and social workers from each area team. The meetings are used to discuss new admissions and transfers and have served a useful purpose, but the basic problems remain. Particular causes for resentment on the part of social services staff are the impossibility of getting patients admitted to the day hospital unless they can provide their own transport, and the paucity of information made available after someone has been admitted for assessment. 'We are just told what medication is recommended and any particular nursing procedures which should be used. There is no diagnosis or prognosis, no help in assessing the patients in terms of priority for a longstay bed and little advice on management problems.' For their part, ESMI staff find the social work reports from the largely untrained staff in the area teams inadequate, and some feel that the specialist homes should have more 'trained staff' (ie RMN-trained nurses). They feel that this would enable them to cope with aggression and other severe behaviour disorders and ensure people need not be 'shuttled back and forth' between the EMI homes and the ESMI unit. The whole situation is in marked contrast to the excellent relationships which have been built up between the SSD and the geriatric service, culminating in the opening of a joint-funded residential home which has a high level of NHS input and cares for very dependent people.

Field social services
Stockport formed eight domiciliary care teams in 1979 which look after elderly and handicapped people, two in each of the four areas into which the borough is divided. The two teams which serve the Vernon House catchment area each consist of a senior social worker, two qualified social workers, one social worker assistant and four social services officers. The latters' main role is to assess for domiciliary services, but they are often also used to do social work tasks. In addition, there is a home help organiser, a rehabilitation officer and a number of 'community support workers' who co-ordinate support for carers in a 'patch' system based on electoral wards. In general, the system works well, but, there is confusion about who is responsible for people receiving DDD services, and the lack of trained staff is a serious drawback. In these circumstances, the senior social workers are not yet in a position to develop better integration between field services and Vernon House.

General practitioners
Because Vernon House residents are drawn from the immediate locality, they are able to retain their own GPs and there are currently no less than 23 coming into the home. This makes the handling of repeat prescriptions and the arrangement of routine

medical check-ups extremely difficult. The OIC would welcome a GP attachment if the person concerned was knowledgeable and interested in this field, but the Family Practitioner Committee is said to be opposed to attachments of this kind. In view of the very important supportive role which GPs play in many of the establishments described in this study this situation seems regrettable. *Home life: a code of practice for residential care* recommends that residents should be able to retain their own GPs if this is practicable, but there does seem to be a strong case for using one practice to provide medical support in specialist homes.

Community nursing service
There is a community nurse attached to the home and the service she provides is very greatly valued.

Summary
Most of the establishments described in this study are recently opened and have all the advantages associated with freshly-equipped premises and hand-picked staff. However, Vernon House shows that it *is* possible to take a home whose previous regime had many retrograde features, and gradually build up a quality of care which is remarkably good when the low level of staffing and very high dependency levels are taken into consideration. It has been and remains an uphill struggle, but it does show how important it is that authorities should not allow themselves to become resigned to poor quality provision on the grounds that a situation has become irreversible. However, the lack of partnership between Stockport SSD and the ESMI unit is a classic instance of wasted resources. A more effective job could be done at Vernon House if the professional expertise available in the OT, nursing and psychology staff in the unit could be brought into the home, cross-training programmes set up, and the ESMI assessments made more helpful. Finally, it must be said that, although the DDD respite care facility has been useful in providing an extra 120 hours of much needed care staff, it is evident that such units should not be tacked onto existing establishments without much more careful consideration of their overall place in service provision and their potential effect on staff and residents.

FERRARD HOUSE
32 Station Road, Antrim, Northern Ireland:
Tel–Antrim 62773

Principal characteristics
Ferrard House, an attractive purpose-built, single storey 'race track' home was opened in 1970 and provides 31 beds, mainly in single rooms, with the additional use of a former staff bungalow for therapeutic groups and rehabilitation. Its role is a combination of assessment, rehabilitation and longstay care for 'confused', physically active people whose behaviour is too difficult for them to be managed elsewhere. It has a sophisticated and carefully structured programme of group therapy, individual support and goal planning, combined with a quite exceptional in-service staff training programme, and commitment to family involvement in care. There are interesting points of comparison with the experimental unit in High Wycombe (page 15) and also with Williamwood House and Woodside.

History
The building, which was carefully planned for its purpose, was the pioneer specialist local authority home in Northern Ireland, and has provided a model for its successors (see page 35). Until 1983 when a new OIC, Yvonne Bakewell was appointed, it was providing good quality supportive care for severe dementia sufferers with virtually no movement of residents except by death: 'It had practically become a hospice'. The new OIC, who is trained in psychotherapeutic nursing and tutoring and is now completing a CSS, has changed the home's role to a much more dynamic model in terms of both assessment and long-term care, and it seems likely that it will develop into a 'resource centre' with a role in improving and sensitising both fieldwork and residential care provision for this client group throughout the authority.

Design and furnishing
Although built on the 'race track' model round a central garden, subsidiary extensions and plentiful daylight from passage skylights and French windows make the atmosphere cheerful and homely compared with many built on this pattern.

Small, light and well-furnished lounges on each corridor resemble those in a good group unit home. The dining room is furnished with circular wooden tables and 'Windsor' chairs and there are flowers on the tables, most of which are fully laid at meal times, so that it could well be a hotel dining room. A good-sized staff office which is separate from, but close to, the OIC's office provides a base for staff handover and training sessions, and for record-keeping (an unusual facility) and another small room near the front door allows for private and uninterrupted individual interviews. The system of staff training and deployment means that a qualified member of staff is always on duty at night so that 'sleeping in' is not necessary, so a disused staff bungalow which adjoins the home provides valuable additional rooms for focused group activity as well as a kitchen for practice cooking sessions and the provision of late breakfasts. It is hoped, when funds permit, to fence and landscape an extensive surrounding grassy area. The front door is kept locked but movement within the unit is free.

Ability range of residents
Ferrard House residents represent the whole range of ability. Of the 24 residents present at the time of the visit, twelve have virtually no cognitive capacity (score 9–11) but seven scored 3–6 (moderately confused) and two were 'lucid' or 'marginal' (0 and 2 respectively). The overall average of 7.7 is therefore misleading. The range reflects Ferrard House's developing role in assessment and rehabilitation and its concern with people suffering from functional mental disorder as well as dementia. It probably also reflects the legacy of the previous regime. Some of the most disabled residents, including one who requires total physical care, are waiting for transfer to hospital because they require nursing care, or because of behavioural characteristics which are causing danger or distress to residents. The wide range of disability both enables and necessitates the carefully structured and graded group therapy system, and it also makes it possible to admit people for assessment without too much concern that they will be distressed by their surroundings if their level of functioning turns out to be relatively good.

However, as at Woodside, emphasis on the assessment function does raise questions about the status in the home of the very dependent people who would otherwise be in hospital. The tendency, often noted in the course of preparing this report, for staff skills and enthusiams to be focussed on the most rewarding group of clients is perhaps being shown here also.

Philosophy

The stated objectives of the home are to:

- individualise all aspects of care
- encourage clients to maintain optimum independence
- maintain familial and community links
- show sensitivity in coping with the dignity of an elderly person
- promote an understanding of this client group and its needs in the wider community.

'Confusion' by itself is not sufficient ground for admission since the home is intended for people who are 'in an agitated state and/or exhibiting abhorrent social behaviour which could not be managed in a conventional unit'. No-one is admitted until it is certain that any alternative form of care has been fully considered and ruled out, and they must be 'highly mobile without the use of aids' and not be doubly incontinent (this refers to incontinence which cannot be managed or controlled). All admissions are initially for assessment with the hope of re-establishing the client in a non-specialist setting of some kind.

Staffing

Staff levels

The staffing system at Ferrard House is of exceptional interest for a number of reasons. The OIC and her deputy are not involved in routine care-giving since they see their skills as being properly used in assessment, staff training, innovation and evaluation, and the management of individuals who, for one reason or another, require particularly skilled personal care. These roles are discussed further below. There is, however, a grade of senior care staff (including the third in charge) who are capable of taking full responsibility, and one of these is on duty at all times. The establishment for this grade is 4.47 wte for day duty (7.50 am– 10.15 pm) and 2.0 wte for night duty. However, the in-service training system (see below) has provided six care assistants (three on day duty and three on night) who are capable of 'acting up' during staff sickness or absence and are paid appropriately when they do. (These members of staff are also ready for promotion to senior posts in other homes.) The establishment for care assistants is 11.46 wte for day care and 3.46 for night care, giving a day care staff/resident ratio of 20.5 hours a week (excluding the OIC and deputy). This is unusually high for a local authority home and allows a minimum of two carers and a senior to be on duty throughout the day, with a third carer usually available in the morning and a double shift overlapping from 2 to 4 pm. This overlap period is used for staff training, one-to-one therapy, outings and assessment work and is seen as vital to the home's system of care. The day care staff are divided into three 'teams' each led by a key worker for a third of the residents. One member of each team is always on duty enabling consistent care and pursuit of agreed goals.

This level of staffing has been obtained partly through a slight increase on the usual establishment for SSD homes, but much more significantly by creating care assistant posts at the expense of other aspects of staffing. As was noted above 'sleeping in' has been eliminated, and a decision to buy-in main meals from a nearby hospital has made it possible to do without the two cooks who would normally be employed. The food provided from the hospital kitchen is felt to be as good and varied as could be cooked in-house, and because of bulk-buying it is also cheaper. The mental disability of Ferrard House residents prevents them from involvement in food planning and preparation so having a cook on the staff is felt to be less important than it would be in a non-specialist home. 2.3 wte catering assistants provide breakfast, serve meals and wash-up and the kitchen in the staff bungalow is available for small-scale cooking. The domestic staff has also been cut from 4 to 3 wte (plus a full-time laundress), the shortfall being made up by enhanced flexibility of care staff and the use of mentally handicapped volunteers from a nearby Adult Training Centre for tasks such as bedmaking. Families who live near enough are encouraged to help their own members if they require intensive care during sickness and to escort them if they require professional services outside the home.

In contrast to many of the homes reported in this study, the OIC prefers full-time staff. She feels that part-timers are more likely to have divided loyalties between their domestic and work responsibilities and to see their work as 'a nice little job' to supplement the family income rather than a skilled and demanding potential career. Too many part-time workers also make it difficult to maintain continuity of care, are confusing for residents, and are not easily fitted into the training programme. A lot of part-time workers were employed when she took over, but the hours of those who were seriously interested in the work were gradually built up to full-time as posts became available and part-timers were not replaced. There are now only two left and they are getting near retirement age and are content to carry out traditional care assistant roles and 'slot in' as and when they are needed.

Staff qualifications and training
All care staff go through an induction process during their first month with each item ticked, signed and dated. This is exceptionally detailed and is therefore quoted in full:

First day: orientation and geographical layout of building; find appliances; health and safety responsibilities; evacuation of building; confidentiality; who's who in group; channels of communication; rota, breaks, clock card, annual leave; lifting techniques; sickness policy.

First/second week: work with experienced care assistant: routine of daily care and residents' names; aim of residential care; primary worker systems; programmes of care; care evaluation; reporting and recording.

Third week: Skills associated with: admission of a client—reception, family support, use of a daily living fact sheet (see Appendix 2); unit orientation; care of the ill resident; care of the dying.

Fourth week: role of care staff in different group settings ie: internal to unit and external to unit; personal assessment and development.

After staff members have been in post for a year the OIC discusses their progress at a special interview, and their suitability for and interest in further training to senior level is considered. If this is agreed they begin a three month in-service course divided into two six-week periods. Topics covered in the first six weeks are mainly related to practical aspects of care under the supervision of the deputy OIC. At the end of the six weeks the student, along with the senior care staff and the OIC, evaluate what has been achieved and decide whether to continue with the second half of the training. This is more related to management skills and is directly supervised by the OIC who uses a wide range of teaching techniques (based on Bloom's Taxonomy of Learning) which are designed to enable the student to obtain, understand, practice and conceptualise the knowledge required. All this training is closely linked to ordinary work under the supervision of the senior care staff on duty, while the overlap period in the afternoon gives an opportunity for theoretical teaching and specific instruction. The topics covered in the courses are listed below:

Weeks 1–6
Administration of medication within Board policy: allow observation; ensure full knowledge of prescription/drug sheets; renewing drugs; safe-keeping of drugs; discontinued drugs.

Health and safety issues: ensure full knowledge of legislation; have working knowledge of communicating systems; understand implication for staff training; security and safety of environment.

Incidents—accidents: reporting; recording; evaluation and prevention.

Care planning: identifying needs; evaluating from progress report; senior participation in primary care team; assessment process.

Staff management: supervision of staff; delegation of workload; identify training needs; staff morale; discipline procedure; grievance procedure; fair allocation of rotas; liaising with other bodies seeking work experience, for example, Youth Training Programmes, schools; liaising with different professional bodies; attending staff meetings and in-service training; maintaining records; admission procedure; death procedure; referred residents, eg money and property; unitary monies.

In-house training and recommended reading is 'topped up' by attendance at relevant short courses run by the social services department. When the course has been satisfactorily completed students take responsibility as a senior staff member in charge of the home under the supervision of the 'real' senior until everyone is fully satisfied that they can cope in all circumstances. They are then regarded as qualified to 'act up' and are paid accordingly when required to do so.

This personal training system runs alongside on-going staff training programmes for both care assistants and seniors. These are divided into spring and autumn 'terms' in which the OIC and her deputy and other trained staff participate as teachers (the presentation of material as a teacher being part of the learning process). Outside specialists are also brought in.

Much emphasis is placed on the use of a half-hour handover session at the beginning of each afternoon, the maintenance of detailed case notes for each client, a weekly review with each 'team' of care workers and regular personal supervision sessions for senior carers. These topics are covered in more detail below. The constant, on-going evaluation of care and therapeutic activity is seen as part of a corporate self-training exercise in which responsibility is shared between everyone concerned.

Regime
Late identification of Ferrard House as a suitable focus for a main case study made it impossible to visit and observe care during the late evening and early morning, or to observe a meal being taken. There is, however, no reason to doubt that the staff are successful in achieving one of the home's basic objectives, which is to continue individual patterns of daily living as far as possible and to adapt toiletting and all other routines to individual needs. The key tool in this endeavour is 'The Ferrard Fact Sheet for Daily Living' (see Appendix 2) which is completed by the key worker during the admission process with the assistance of relatives, home help and so on.

Having the same number of staff on duty at all times (apart from the afternoon overlap period) makes it easier to ensure complete flexibility in relation to getting up and going to bed. If breakfast is required after 10 am it can be cooked by a care assistant in the staff bungalow. Main meals are ordered from the hospital kitchen in accordance with known tastes and needs. Six alternatives are available at each meal with rotation on a four-weekly cycle, and different menus are provided in summer and winter. The staff recognise religious festivals and days of special observance when making their choice, and wine is served on major festivals, all of which helps maintain awareness of external reality. The food ordered also takes account of the extent to which anxiety and agitation burn up extra calories since the OIC believes that residents require a higher than normal intake of carbohydrate and vitamin B. The hospital kitchen is always prepared to make a special effort for a party. (At a Saint Patrick's Day celebration, everything served was green!)

Residents who are able to do so collect their meals from the hatch on a self-service basis and sit at properly-laid tables. Those who need a lot of assistance sit at other tables and are helped by staff sitting beside them after the main meal has been served.

It is found that it is better to have three rather than four residents to each table as this gives more space and discourages interference with a neighbour's food.

Activities
A great deal of effort is expended on maintaining a daily programme of small group activity which is carefully geared to each resident's ability, care objectives and mental state at particular times of day. Groups cover RO, reminiscence, self help, crafts, musical appreciation and keep fit, but these titles belie the amount of detailed work which goes into particular programmes. For example a group geared towards rehabilitation and discharge uses 'personal history' photograph albums, compiled with the help of relatives, to promote orientation. Reminiscence groups make use of collected and borrowed items of special interest with a different focus each week—old china, old cooking implements and so on. The RO 'news' session is based on local papers reporting events in residents' home towns. Music sessions, which are geared to personal taste (and include classical music) are also used to promote mood changes such as relaxation or stimulation. Some residents go regularly to a community-based musical appreciation group. Staff are encouraged to keep a constant check on whether the groups are serving their objectives, and they may be subjected to an attempt at formal evaluation. For example, over a six-week period, three groups of matched residents were given respectively intensive RO; occupational therapy only; and neither RO nor OT; and their performance was measured at the beginning and the end of the period.

These structured group activities move naturally towards external involvement. A newspaper item about a forthcoming flower show, for example, may lead to an outing by a small group of residents interested in gardening. Relatives and friends are encouraged to involve residents in previous activities and interests and sometimes the home can play an active part in this. For example, the local Women's Institute meets in the homes of its members, and one of the residents takes her turn in playing host as well as going out to meetings elsewhere. Outings are tailor-made to residents' tastes and interests as far as possible and large group expeditions are avoided. Transport is usually by private car or taxi.

Sometimes an even more individual programme has to be devised. At the time of the visit, for example, it was discovered that one resident, who had become increasingly withdrawn and apathetic, resented deprivation of daily domestic activity; she improved quite remarkably when (after consulting the unions and line management) it became possible to involve her in routine domestic work on a regular basis.

Involvement with relatives
Much emphasis is put on involving relatives with decision-making at every stage in a resident's career and in sharing the caring insofar as this is possible and appropriate. Staff are trained in understanding inter-generational family dynamics and the experiences of anger, grief and loss which arise from coping with dementia. The OIC sees it as part of her job to contribute at a local relatives' support group and to be available to advise and support carers who are still coping, as well as to train and assist other health care and social services staff who are carrying out this role.

Assessment, goal planning and reviews
The Ferrard 'Social Assessment Programme' for new residents lists a formidable range of assessment tools including the Clifton Assessment Procedures for the Elderly (CAPE), an exhaustive checklist of self help, personal and social skills, and copies of tests for verbal orientation, personal and current information, and concentration. The full barrage is only used when people have been admitted with the specific objective of assessment, otherwise the tests are used on a selective basis. A month after admission the results of the assessment are reviewed and recommendation are made for further rehabilitation, placement elsewhere, or continuing care at Ferrard House. If it is agreed, either at this conference or later, that rehabilitation and discharge are possible a planned process is worked out and goals are set which are evaluated at the weekly meetings of the primary care team. There is strong emphasis on maintaining the involvement of the family, the community social worker and other relevant professionals in the process, which allows a gradual introduction to the new placement and a phased decrease of contact after the transfer of responsibility for care has been made. Final discharge from the Ferrard House 'case load' is not expected to take place until four to six weeks after a client ceases to be a resident. There is inevitably a degree of ambivalence about undertaking rehabilitation since the better the therapeutic relationship with the client and her family and the more successful

the process, the more distressing it is to have to work towards its termination. (This conflict is also evident at Williamwood House.)

More commonly the client will remain at Ferrard House but a chart giving each resident's problems of daily living—physical, social and behavioural—along with the objectives of care and the plan for care, is filed in a clear plastic folder facing the page on which the resident's daily progress is recorded. Each record is discussed every week by the primary care team and, if necessary, goals modified in the light of experience. Completed pages of the record are transferred to the resident's personal file. At any one time, one or two residents are likely to be in an intensive personal care programme in which the OIC is heavily involved, either as a personal care giver (particularly if a resident is especially difficult or disruptive) or as a supervisor.

Help and advice on behavioural therapy is available from a psychologist in devising such detailed care plans and the psycho-geriatrician, who drops in at least once a week, is always available for consultation.

Community-based assessment and the admission process
Domiciliary assessment, on referral from a field social worker, is an integral part of the OIC's role and may well lead to a decision to provide on-going support and care which does not involve admission. Suitability for admission is determined by the presence of behaviour which is too difficult or disruptive to manage elsewhere rather than the level of dementia *per se*, so that functionally-ill people and those suffering from behaviour disorders may be accepted. Physically disabled people and those whose dementia is already so advanced that they are not likely to benefit from Ferrard House are not considered suitable, and neither are those who can at least be given a trial elsewhere. The clinical judgement of the psychogeriatrician is a valued part of the assessment process, but the decision to admit remains with the SSD, and the OIC is determined that Ferrard House should not act merely as a halfway house between ordinary residential care and a longstay psychiatric ward. If admission is decided upon, the leader of one of the three teams of care assistants, who will act as key worker, visits the client's home to establish relationships with the client and family, accumulate the information required in the 'Fact Sheet for Daily Living' and arrange the admission process.

Professional support services

Because the visit was undertaken during the Easter holidays it was not possible to meet the supporting psychiatrist or psychologist, but it was clear that relationships, though close and friendly, were firmly based on professional equality. In general the home follows a policy in which clients receive professional treatment in the community rather than bringing professionals into the home, but advice from all relevant professionals is available when required and, as was noted above, they are used to provide staff training sessions. Conversely, Ferrard House is extensively used for training visits by students or workers in other professions, and involvement with field workers over a particular client is used to help them understand the complexity of working with dementia sufferers, identify appropriate referrals, and the use of assessment techniques. Understanding and support of the role of Ferrard House at middle management level in the SSD appears to be exceptionally good and this is undoubtedly a major factor in the very rapid development of its role over the last two years.

Summary

Ferrard House demonstrated, perhaps more clearly than any establishment discussed in this report, what a mine of resources is available in the provision of specialist care if only it can be tapped. Within two years a good, but not exceptional, long-established specialist home providing 'tender loving care' has developed into a unit where the quality of staffing, staff training, assessment procedures and on-going care and rehabilitation is providing a resource for the area. However, one source of concern does persist; the more emphasis is put on the development of assessment and rehabilitation skills and techniques, the less time there will be for residents who cannot benefit from them, and the greater the likelihood of such residents 'falling over the edge' into psychiatric hospital care. Either that care must be made so good that this does not matter, or social services must ensure that 'the best' does not drive out 'the good' in its own specialist provision.

WOODSIDE
40 Woodside Road, Selly Oak, Birmingham:
Tel–Birmingham 472 8770

Principal characteristics
Woodside is a 30-bedded local authority home whose current official role is to provide shortstay beds for assessment and respite care, together with very flexible day care. Strictly speaking, therefore, it should not have been included in this study. For a long time, however (due to the 'silting-up' of the assessment beds), it was, in practice, a longstay care home, and the potential and problems of its present mode of operation are of considerable interest to anyone concerned in this field. In particular, its effective use of unqualified staff in the assessment process, its success in operating with minimal psychogeriatric support services, its relaxed regime, and its use as a staging post in the placement of people in non-specialist care, all have implications for this study.

History
Woodside was opened in 1977 as a pioneering, specialist unit intended to provide 20 assessment beds and ten longstay beds. Within two years, however, the number of residents requiring longstay care who could not be transferred elsewhere had risen to 23 and in October 1980 its official use was changed to 20 longstay beds, eight assessment, and two rota care. This combined use became more and more problematic because the longstay residents inevitably became more disabled and the contrast between their needs, and those of people requiring assessment and respite care, became much more marked, making the defence of the ten shortstay beds increasingly difficult. In the spring of 1984 the Social Services Committee decided to empty Woodside of its longstay residents by transferring them to another home, Bourn House, which was newly designated EMI.

Five longstay residents remained at Woodside at the time of the visit because it was felt that they could not be managed at Bourn House and the Woodside beds were already silting up again. If an assessment unit is to do its proper job, it is clearly essential to provide enough specialist longstay beds to take those who, after assessment, are considered to need specialist care.

Design and furnishing
The single-storey building has three wings running at right angles
from the entrance lobby which is a popular sitting area. One of
these provides the dining room (subdivisible by a movable
partition), kitchen, an unusually large laundry, office and staff
room. The office is a large pleasant room which was originally
a lounge. The previous office was very small and there was
constant conflict between residents' need to wander in and out
at will and the staff's need to get on with their work. Staff were
very reluctant to create aggression and anxiety by forbidding the
residents access. In the new office they can come and go without
causing disruption. (The need for people with dementia to be
able to maintain this reassuring contact with staff is an important
design point and is discussed further on page 54.) The main sitting
room is on the other side of the entrance lobby and has doors
leading into the lobby and into one of the bedroom wings. This
permits use of the lounge as a passage and, since it 'cuts a corner',
there is a considerable movement through the lounge, and this
seems to encourage a sense of involvement and staff contact with
residents. A further small lounge which was previously the office
is not much used. There are three double and 24 single rooms
divided between the two bedroom wings. It is hoped, eventually,
to keep one wing for assessment and the other for respite care
attenders. There are nine WCs arranged in blocks, and two
bathrooms. A room has been fitted up as a small kitchen for
residents' use and rehabilitation training. The front door is kept
locked with the key hanging inside.

In general the design is functional but not exceptional or
particularly attractive.

Ability range of residents
Woodside's current use as an assessment and respite care centre
means that levels of disability change from week to week and so
no attempt was made to complete the CRBRS scale. The 'old'
longstay residents are, however, very severely disabled, both
physically and mentally, and several require total care. There are
considerable difficulties in combining care for this group with
that of respite care attenders, whose levels of disability vary
a good deal, and of people admitted for assessment, who may
not be suffering from dementia at all. The mix can only be coped
with because of the flexible nature of the regime and its strong
emphasis on observation of individual need.

Philosophy

Woodside was a pioneer in the concept of fitting the regime to the needs and abilities of residents with dementia rather than trying to make them adapt to the regime, and the current OIC continues to practice this tradition with enthusiasm. The walls of the office are hung with basic statements of principle arranged as mnemonics.

For example

TEAMWORK

To accept each other's contribution
Each of us have different qualities
And by pooling each others' resources
Main aims and objectives are met

While some see physical needs
Others see emotional and spiritual
Revealing skills which when put together produce the
Key to team work.

KEY WORKER

Knowing in depth their history before reception
Each has a right to live as near to their own lifestyle as possible
You soon find a growing friendship between residents, staff and relatives

Welcome the resident on their reception
Observe their reaction to their new environment
Record their progress or deterioration
Keep a close eye and keen
Ear, they will soon identify you as a friend
Remember everyone needs to trust someone.

Virtually any type of disability can be coped with except 'spontaneous severe aggression'—that is 'aggression arising from inner torment rather than as a response to being pressured into activity'.

Staffing
Staff levels
When Woodside was opened its staffing level was little better than the Birmingham norm of one staff member to 20 residents. This proved to be totally impractical and after 18 months it was

doubled to a ratio of one to ten. There are now three senior officers and 640 care staff hours a week (including night staff) giving a day-time average of 16.2 care staff hours per resident week. This seems appallingly low for the nature of the work, especially in view of staff involvement in domiciliary visits and assessment procedures. All but four of the staff are part-time which is found to increase flexibility and lessen the strain of the work.

Staff qualifications and training
No present member of staff has professional qualifications, although the OIC, Teresa Clements, is used to supervising CSS students and has had members of staff who obtained the CSS. She herself is about to start a CQSW course. She prefers to recruit inexperienced care staff 'who have no expectations of the client group' and train them herself. Attitudes are, she feels, far more important than qualifications, though it is necessary for staff to have sufficient basic education to complete assessment records and present their findings competently at case conferences. All Birmingham homes are expected to base their training on an SSD staff manual entitled *Homes for the elderly: role of care assistant: analysis of tasks* which is a detailed and comprehensive document with a strong emphasis on the quality of care giving. This is used during the induction process of new staff at Woodside, and a part of every staff meeting is also deliberately used for training purposes. Care staff may also attend a day release course at Bournville College which lasts twelve weeks, and may follow this with a year-long day-release training. They will then be considered for secondment to the CSS or CQSW courses.

Staff communication
General communication is through handover sessions, the maintenance of Kardex records and informal chatting. The main focus is on providing information about particular residents to the key worker concerned. Detailed toileting charts and 'sleep profile' charts are maintained for those who need them.

Regime
Getting up and going to bed
The OIC emphasises the importance of maintaining independence in the getting up process, especially with assessment clients. Staff encourage residents who are awake to sit up, help them take off their night clothes and then leave them, with washing

things to hand and clothes put out, while they attend to the next resident, coming back at intervals to monitor and assist in the dressing process. People are taken to breakfast as soon as they are ready. Going to bed is completely flexible and over half the residents were still up at 10.30 pm on the day of the visit. It is seen as an important part of the assessment process to identify bed-time habits and pass this information on if the resident is to be transferred to another home. If a resident prefers to doze all night in a chair, this is perfectly acceptable.

Meals

Breakfast is a staggered meal with places being laid as residents arrive. Only one table is fully laid. Residents who have been admitted for assessment are seated at this table to begin with, and are assessed for their ability to serve themselves; 'if they get mixed up' they are moved elsewhere. Other meals were not observed, but the main emphasis is on flexibility of place and time of eating. People who prefer to eat in the lounge or in their own rooms can do so—'After all people often eat in the sitting room in their own homes'—and snacks can be provided on request. One resident asked for, and got, a generous-sized glass of sherry in the late evening on the day of the visit.

Activities

There is no 'classroom' RO but involvement in domestic tasks is encouraged, together with board games in small groups, shopping expeditions and one-to-one activity and communication. Occasionally 'we close down the whole home and everyone goes out ot lunch'. Every evening after supper the partition in the dining room is pushed back and a 'party' takes place with dancing and singing, and soft drinks or beer are served from a bar in the corner of the room. Residents come along spontaneously because they are attracted by the music and atmosphere, and the event is seen as being more enjoyable and more genuinely therapeutic than formal 'music and movement' sessions. Holding these 'parties' in the evening means that the senior staff member on duty is likely to be free from administrative chores and so able to take part. The activity also helps to get residents properly tired and ready for a night's sleep.

Clothing

As most residents are now shortstay, clothing is brought in with them and managed in co-operation with their family. The key worker assists with purchases for longer-stay residents if necessary. Woodside has an exceptionally large and well-planned laundry room.

Bathing
Bathing is arranged to fit in with established habits as far as possible.

Management of incontinence
By day: Residents are normally taken to the toilet at around 9 am, 12.45 pm, 3 pm and 6 pm. A chart is kept in all WCs and filled in each time it is used. The data is then collated so that a detailed record of each resident's habits is built up, and this information is then used to establish a more individual pattern of toiletting and minimise incontinence. Pads are used if necessary but are not usually required.

By night: Mölnlycke pads and pants are used extensively at night. This is expensive but said to be worth it because the laundry bill is very much reduced and residents do not have to be disturbed by a toilet round.

Involvement with relatives
The assessment process puts very strong emphasis on the development of a positive relationship with relatives, and this is continued throughout the period of contact. There is no relatives' group but they are invited to parties from time to time and are involved in outings and other activities. Key workers are encouraged to sit with relatives and the resident concerned during visits if it is felt that this will help communication and ease tension.

Day care and respite care
Woodside provides integrated day care for up to five clients daily. The emphasis is on complete flexibility of hours. Clients may come before breakfast or not until the early evening when carers want an evening out. In the latter case they may be undressed and got into a dressing gown so that the carer only has to put them into bed when they are taken home. Day care is also provided at weekends on both a regular and occasional basis. Many of those receiving day care are also recipients of respite care so that a great deal of their time is spent at Woodside.

Respite care is seen as a key aspect of Woodside's current role and in theory ten beds are allocated to it, usually for use on a month-in, month-out basis. However, because of the remaining five longstay residents and one 'blocked' place, only four respite beds were available at the time of the visit.

Assessment and admission procedures

In the absence of an NHS psychogeriatric assessment unit, Woodside has taken over this role and seems to be carrying it out very effectively using unqualified care staff. Anyone who is referred as requiring assessment is visited at home by a member of the senior staff and the proposed key worker in order to observe the home environment and family relationships, and obtain a full understanding of the reasons for referral. If necessary, more than one visit will be paid. The desirability or otherwise of an assessment admission is then discussed at a case conference to which relatives and other involved community-based supporters—such as home help, volunteer visitor and community nurse—are invited, along with the relevant field social worker.

If an assessment admission is considered to be desirable this is normally for a four to six week period. The admission is carefully managed by the key worker who becomes responsible for detailed observation. 'Areas of observation' include: medication; emotional state—shown physically and verbally; awareness of surroundings; concentration and communication; anti-social habits; orientation; level of dependence on staff/relations; management problem areas and general health. A detailed sleep chart and toiletting chart is maintained. A simple 'orientation questionnaire' and a recognition test using pictures of familiar objects are completed on the domiciliary visit, halfway through the assessment period and at its end, but they are not used if there are signs that the resident is distressed either by failing to recognise objects or because they feel the tests are childish and demeaning.

At the end of the assessment period there is a further case conference at which the key worker summarises the conclusions she has reached about the resident and recommends future placement. This may be long-term care in a specialist or non-specialist home (with or without discharge until a bed becomes available); respite care; day care; or return home with appropriate domiciliary support. About half those who are assessed do return home, but they are not discharged until agreed support services have been laid on. If a resident has been discharged to another home, the staff are given detailed information about her habits and tastes and, if necessary, the key worker may accompany her and stay with her for a short time to help her settle down and to show the new care staff how care can best be provided. However, both the information and the proffered help may be ignored, sometimes with disastrous results.

This method of assessment has been successful on a number of occasions in identifying people who were not suffering from a dementing illness, and a psychologist has found that the conclusions reached by the key worker correlate with those obtained by using the CAPE assessment scale (see page 151). (The home would like to use the CAPE scale on a routine basis but finds the cost of buying copies prohibitive.) The operation of this system has been made more flexible by Birmingham SSD's move from generic patch-based fieldwork teams to specialised teams dealing with particular client groups. This has made it much easier to 'cut corners' in the admission process since the OIC can admit on her own authority without a social worker's assessment and she can also undertake joint domiciliary visits with the social worker if this is appropriate.

The Woodside assessment process appears to be an innovation of great importance in this field in that it relates assessment to the whole person and not just to their mental state, and it provides detailed information for carers which is relevant regardless of where that care is being provided. Properly used it should make appropriate and lasting placements in non-specialist homes easier, and ensure that specialist places are only used for those who really need them because of particular management difficulties. The fact that this work is being carried out by staff with no professional qualifications and minimal access to psychiatric services does raise the question as to whether psychogeriatric assessment units on the traditional (expensive) pattern are really necessary. However the system is only workable if enough specialist and non-specialist longstay beds are available to take those who are considered to need them without delay. At present half of the 13 assessment beds are occupied by people awaiting longstay places.

Professional support services
General practitioner
One GP looks after long-term residents and those shortstay residents who live too far for their own GP to be called in while they are at Woodside. He is an enthusiastic supporter of the home's philosophy and sees it as an important part of his role

to assess the appropriateness of the medication which temporary residents are receiving and to liaise with their own GP about future care needs when the resident returns home.

Psychiatric services
There is no specialist psychogeriatric service in this part of Birmingham and facilities for assessment or respite care are minimal. Some time ago a generic psychiatrist based in Rubery Hill psychiatric hospital took an interest in Woodside and visited once a week on a voluntary basis, and this was found to be extremely helpful. At present, however, there is no regular contact with a psychiatrist. A psychologist based at the local geriatric hospital does visit for two hours weekly, but her involvement is at present at a fairly superficial level. The OIC would like to have a psychologist who 'worked alongside' care staff and could help them sort out management issues. However, this psychologist has started a forum called 'Elderly Persons in the Community' (EPIC) which is open to all professionals who provide services in this field and this has proved to be useful in improving understanding and communication.

Community nursing service
At the time of the visit the community nursing service and the psychiatric community nurses, who had previously been based in Rubery Hill Hospital, had just moved into a refurbished health centre and were developing plans for a new style of work, but neither group had yet had much contact with Woodside.

Social services
The SSD was also in the process of reorganising its services for the elderly at the time of the visit. As was noted above, it has moved from generic patch teams to specialist teams, and the team manager concerned with services to the elderly in this area is building up a close relationship with the Woodside staff. In policy terms, the department is putting its main emphasis on the provision of EMI day care places in centres attached to residential homes, the improvement of the availability and flexibility of the home help service, and the subdivision of the many large Part III establishments to create a more domestic atmosphere and improve the quality of care.

Summary
Woodside illustrates the potential of homes specialising in shortstay care and really flexible day care within the EMI field.

It is also of key importance because it functions successfully with minimal psychiatric support services and has, in fact, set up an assessment service in the vacuum left by the NHS. It illustrates the constant effort needed to keep shortstay beds open, and the longstay residential resources needed to achieve this. It seems evident that *if* homes of this kind can keep their beds open, they may provide a really valuable and cost-effective resource.

National Health Service

DOVE HOUSE
The Gloucester Centre, Morpeth Close, Orton Longville, Peterborough PE2 0JU: Tel–Peterborough 232321

Principal characteristics
Dove House is an NHS establishment providing 16 longstay beds and six shortstay ones in a single storey building which is part of a complex mainly used for housing people with mental handicaps. A similar building on the same site is used by the NHS for specialist day care. The charge nurse at Dove House, Willie Kwa, is strongly concerned to provide a domestic and relaxed lifestyle for the longstay patients, and friendly and accessible emergency and respite care. There has, however, been some tension between these objectives and traditional NHS practice and administration. Dove House therefore offers an interesting example of the difficulties likely to be encountered by the many health authorities who are seeking to provide longstay care for dementia sufferers in small, localised units. Another area of interest is the relationship between Dove House and the neighbouring day hospital, and the difficulties encountered in using the latter for the benefit of longstay residents.

History
In 1981 the Peterborough HA found itself with a building in the Gloucester Centre, which it could not afford to use to house mentally handicapped people, and with a desperate need for some longstay psychogeriatric beds. It was therefore decided to use Dove House for this purpose on a temporary basis—but with considerable misgivings about the implications of mixing psychogeriatrics with mental handicap. A new DGH was being planned with a psychiatric wing and it was intended to close Dove House when beds became available in the hospital. For the first three years the development of Dove House was left almost entirely to the charge nurse, under the very relaxed supervision of the senior nursing officer for mental handicap. Control was then taken over by the Peterborough Hospital Unit Management Team and subsequently by the Psychiatric Nursing Division

which has now become a sector on its own. Although the psychogeriatrician and the chairman of the HA are both very supportive there was, initially, pressure to conform to established management and administrative practices. The mutually helpful relationships which had been established with the rest of the Gloucester Centre—which included sharing holidays and entertainments—ceased, but facilities for staff training and recruitment and the availability of clerical support have improved. Dove House does, however, continue to enjoy a considerable degree of independence, but it is still intended to close it when the DGH beds are available.

Design and furnishing
The single storey building consists of two wings joined by a passage, which has the front door on one side, and the kitchen, dining areas, office and interview room on the other. It was originally intended to house two groups of eleven mentally handicapped people, each with their own lounge and other facilities, and with a dining area divided by the kitchen. When it was first opened one of the lounges was used for day activities for 15 residents and five day attenders and the other was used in the evenings. When the nearby day hospital opened, day care ceased and the number of short and longstay residents was built up to 22, which was too many for one lounge. Supervision in two lounges on different sides of the building was not feasible, so one large bedroom was converted into a second lounge and one lounge into a bedroom. Though the two lounges are now adjoining, supervision from one to the other is not easy and consideration is being given to making an opening between them. One lounge is designated 'the quiet room', although it houses the TV and is in fact used for the more noisy and disturbed patients. There are three single bedrooms (used for shortstay), two two-bedded, one three-bedded and three four-bedded. Four bathrooms are provided—two on each wing—but staff complain that design, lifting facilities and the relation of the bath to the WC are not suitable for very disabled people (although the lifting equipment is of the type recommended for NHS units). There are also two single WCs. Lavish provision of full-height windows lets in plenty of light and sun but the general effect is bare and utilitarian—very good for a hospital but poor for a home. The bedrooms, though carpeted in Flotex, are minimally furnished with very little in the way of ornaments, personal possessions, storage space or provision for personal privacy. Residents do not have access to them during the day, the doors being bolted. Some

wallpaper has been put up in the lounge on the charge nurse's personal initiative, and a chiming clock had just been bought with a donation given in memory of a patient, but apart from this, a radio/record player and a piano there is little furnishing except chairs. Redecoration is urgently needed and is in the process of being approved. The surrounding campus is grassy and pleasant and, since Dove House is some distance from a public road, the door is not kept locked and patients can go out by themselves with an eye being kept on them. It is hoped to make one area an enclosed garden when funds permit.

Ability range of residents

The overall score for longstay patients at the time of the visit was 7.1 with a range from 3–11. Four patients had scores of 10 or 11 and thus virtually no cognitive function; the most able was a new admission who was still being assessed. One is thought to be suffering from 'hysterical blindness' allied to a difficult and dependent personality, one has dementia superimposed on long-standing schizophrenia and a very active active alert-looking man with an early dementia is given to almost constant song. Several are noisy in one way or another. There is a high level of physical disability and eight patients are unable to walk without assistance.

Philosophy

An 'operational policy' drawn up by the charge nurse states that:

> 'Staff will adopt the attitude of providing the highest possible standard of care based on daily living. No effort will be spared to the creation of a "domestic home atmosphere" in Dove House. A joint decision between the senior house officer and the nurse-in-charge should be reached before any treatment is carried out. Should there be a need for tranquillisers to be used, only agreed drugs be prescribed and a review made after seven days. Every effort should be made to eliminate possible causes before the use of tranquillisers is considered. As we are not in the business of curing the illness, activities are mainly geared to maintaining the remaining skills of the sufferer or slowing down the process of deterioration of the illness'.

This last sentence reflects the charge nurse's determination to resist any tendency to regard Dove House as a place where treatment is provided rather than as a home. There is, as was noted above, some tension between Kwa's ideals of autonomy and normalisation and customary NHS procedures. Staff are on first name terms, uniform is not worn and flexibility and use of personal initiative is encouraged.

Staffing
Staff levels
The allocation of day time staff is 18.6 wte. This provides 27.1 hours of daytime staff per resident week, with five people per shift. Shifts run from 7.30 am to 3 pm and 1 pm to 9.30 pm. Three people are on duty at night (6.46 wte). The overlap period in the middle of day is seen as being essential for training, staff meetings and taking residents out. There was, however, considerable anxiety at the time of the visit that these levels would be cut by administrators who did not realise the very demanding nature of this job and the importance of having time to give to individual patients.

Staff qualifications and training
Willie Kwa and one of the senior nurses are RMN, the other two are SRN. There are five SENs and the rest of the daytime staff are nursing assistants. Training levels amongst the night staff are similar. All the staff were selected by Kwa and most of them have not worked in a similar setting. He says that he prefers people without experience and therefore without preconceptions. The HA gives a one week induction course for new nursing auxiliaries in which basic routines are covered, and for their first two weeks at Dove House all new staff work alongside a staff member of a similar grade. After a fortnight they have a personal supervision session with Kwa to discuss their responses to their work and their future training needs. Particular events are used to provide opportunities for training. Plans are now being made in the psychiatric sector to provide a rolling programme of training for nursing auxiliaries which will cover all basic aspects of psychiatric nursing in ten modules and will make it easier for nursing auxiliaries to move from one type of ward to another.

Kwa puts a lot of emphasis on encouraging nurses of all grades to put forward ideas for promoting the welfare of individual patients and then to follow them through themselves, learning how to cope with getting necessary permissions, laying on transport and so on. He does not use a key worker system, believing that it would result in staff 'looking after their own' instead of taking responsibility for coping with any need which is observed and feeding back relevant information. This is, however, now under review.

Staff communication

Handover sessions are used for communication and training purposes, and there is a monthly staff meeting to discuss wider aspects of problems and patient care, but in general communication is informal, and patient's records, though correctly maintained, are not very informative about personal matters. There is no 'chatty' occurrence book of the type used at Bemerton Lodge (see page 98) or Orchard House (page 110), but a Mental Health Unit 24-hour ward report is submitted each day and a copy kept on the ward.

Regime

Getting up and going to bed

Early morning tea is taken by night staff to patients who are awake; they are changed if necessary and encouraged to settle again until the day staff start getting them up after 7.30 am. On the day of the visit everyone was dressed and in the middle of breakfast by 9 am except one patient who had had a very restless night and had been left to sleep. At night, undressing and bathing is a gradual process which goes on during the whole evening. Several patients were already in their pyjamas by 7 pm having been undressed in the bathrooms rather than in their bedrooms, but they were then returned to the lounge, and no-one was in bed at 10 pm.

Meals

Adherence to a timetable is demanded by the need to clear the hot lockers, which are sent over from the main Gloucester Centre kitchens, and have them ready for collection. Meals are ordered by a staff member from a range of alternatives and an effort is made to provide some choice to patients and to meet known likes and dislikes, difficulty in chewing and so on. As was noted above, the dining room is divided into two sections by the kitchen and one side is used by the more able eaters who have only one helper, while the other is used by those who need feeding. Plastic disposable aprons are used as necessary and an attempt has been made to brighten the dining room with bright plastic table cloths and gaily-coloured mats. Brandy or Guinness is often provided as an evening drink.

Activities
There are no individual written programmes though staff are aware of individual capabilities and encourage eating, moving and so on accordingly. There is also no attempt at any formal RO—even the almost ubiquitous 'RO Board' giving place, date and weather is absent. An OT aide and a physiotherapist come across from the day hospital twice a week (when they can be spared) to conduct a physical activity session, but the aide is inexperienced and no-one sounds enthusiastic about their success. The patients in for shortstay care are almost always day hospital patients and continue to attend, but the day hospital staff feel that they do not have sufficient resources to accept the longstay patients who are usually more disabled than the rest of their clientele. An effort is, however, made to include individuals in a group if they are thought to be particularly suited for it. There was much more OT involvement with all patients in Dove House when the day hospital was not open and Dove House was providing day care. The tendency for more able patients to draw off resources from the more disabled is again evident here.

The main focus of activity is individual trips outside the home including short walks, visits to the town for window shopping or to make purchases and visits to a pub or restaurant. These are undertaken on staff initiative and there is no planned programme. Hospital transport may be used for these trips with a staff member driving, but the home holds an orange disabled persons badge which staff use when taking patients out in their own cars. There is also a very successful annual holiday (see below).

Clothing
Daytime clothing is bought by relatives if they hold the pension book, or by staff using the patient's personal allowance when there are sufficient funds in their hospital account. Trouble is taken to meet personal tastes and at the time of the visit a coat obtained on approval had just been rejected by the patient concerned and was being returned. There have been major problems in safeguarding clothing because it had to be sent to an unreliable central laundry where things got lost and spoilt, but a lengthy battle to install heavy-duty washing machines had just been won when the visit took place. This would make the care of clothing much easier (if sufficient staff were available to wash them), and also make it possible to provide personal night clothes. At present these are standard hospital issue and male

patients wear pyjamas with the name of the HA prominently stamped across the seat of the trousers.

Bathing
Baths are given weekly, usually in the evening, unless they are required more often.

Management of continence
By day: People are taken to the WC according to individual patterns of need but everyone is toiletted before meals. Mölnlycke pads are used by those who need them. No regular record or chart relating to micturition is kept but there is a 'bath and bowels' book.

By night: At the time of the visit incontinence sheets were used if they were needed and regular checks made to see if they needed changing but Mölnlycke night pads are now used instead. Patients are not woken up to use the WC, but they are assisted if they show signs of wanting to do so.

Reviews
The charge nurse goes through every patient's case notes every four months with the psychogeriatrician and senior house officer and discusses progress and management issues. If the person has settled well and is presenting no serious problems, referral for Part III admission may be considered. However, the shortage of places makes it unlikely that this will be successful, and there is sometimes resistance on the part of relatives because transfer to Part III involves the payment of fees. If the patient is deteriorating a decision may be taken whether prolonged treatment with antibiotics would be appropriate should a chest infection develop. However relatives would always be consulted and their wishes respected. All patients are given a full medical examination every six months.

Personal allowance
This is banked by the HA, with a small float being kept at Dove House. Money is drawn on patients' behalf and used for clothing, personal shopping, outings and holiday expenses.

Outings
In addition to Dove House's policy of encouraging individual outings there is an annual holiday using rented chalets. The most recent was in Wales and earlier ones have been in Yorkshire and

Lowestoft. Sixteen patients (including some shortstay) and eight staff travel in hired self-drive minibuses. Overtime, transport and food costs are paid by the HA having been built into the budget 'when times were easier'. The patients' personal allowance is used to pay the cost of the chalets. These expeditions are said to be very successful. They result in a greatly improved personal response from the patients and also in greater awareness on the part of staff of the strain which relatives endure when providing 24-hour care. Staff and patients who go on holiday are selected on a rota basis so that everyone has an opportunity to take part.

Involvement with relatives

Relatives are encouraged to visit at any time, take patients out and share in treatment decisions. Particular trouble is taken to establish a supportive relationship with the families of patients using respite beds, and they are encouraged not only to use Dove House for unplanned 'granny sitting' but also to telephone at any time to ask for advice and help. The charge nurse will visit patients at home if this seems to be appropriate. However, the main focus of support for relatives is the Community Psychiatric Nursing Service and this is backed up by a local Alzheimer's Disease Society (ADS) (which one of the CPNs helped to get off the ground) supported by a psychogeriatrician and Willie Kwa. This ADS puts much emphasis on arranging social outings for dementia sufferers and relatives since management problems often make social activities difficult for relatives to achieve on their own; it is now also developing volunteer training and mutual support services. Kwa therefore has usually had contact with relatives and carers before a dementia sufferer reaches the point of requiring NHS care, so the movement into care can be gradual and appropriate.

Day care and respite care

In addition to the regular day care provided by the adjoining day hospital and its own respite bed services, Dove House offers known carers a daytime 'granny sitting service' with flexible hours, and it also provides short-notice overnight or weekend care if a bed is available. These arrangements are made by telephoning Kwa who takes pride in the fact that he has never had to refuse either facility, even if the interview room or some other space has had to be pressed into service as a bedroom. In addition, Dove House liaises with the other local longstay dementia unit in St John's Hospital to keep one of their combined stock of respite beds free for emergency use, and this facility has proved invaluable. The remaining five shortstay beds are used for respite care on a planned basis—primarily for patients who are also attending the day hospital. There have been no problems with bed blocking by patients whose relatives refuse to have them back, which is a tribute to the reliability and accessibility of the support offered.

Assessment and admission procedures

All referrals go from the GP to the specialist psychiatrist who normally visits with the CPN to assess and make a joint decision about management and the care package required, which the CPN then implemens. Admission for assessment purposes is kept to a minimum and used mainly for people presenting management problems, such as sleep disturbance or incontinence, or to observe the effect of a drug. Psychological tests and blood tests are done in the patient's home and, if further physical examination is needed, this is undertaken in the day hospital. If respite care or day care is required this is brought to a weekly multi-disciplinary meeting which Kwa attends, though the final decision lies with the consultant. Relatives are always invited to visit Dove House before admission is arranged, though there is no routine visit by Kwa to the patient's home.

Professional support services
Psychogeriatric service
The consultant, Dr R W Williams, works from the ground floor of a large house close to St John's Hospital. This is a small hospital built nearly 60 years ago, in the grounds of the DGH, opposite a large modern geriatric hospital (Fenland House). St John's provides care for 15 severe dementia sufferers, and 16 beds for psychogeriatric patients. Five specialist CPNs have an office adjoining that of Dr Williams. The system therefore offers very easy communication between the consultant, the CPNs, the staff of St John's Hospital and the general public. (Dr Williams' office is also used for meetings of the ADS.) Dove House is some three miles away but Dr Williams and one of the CPNs maintain close contact with it and support Kwa in his efforts to maintain and defend the Dove House regime.

Other medical support
No GP is involved with Dove House but the Senior House Officer visits regularly and is available on request at any time. All nursing procedures are carried out by Dove House staff.

Social services
There is little contact between the psychogeriatric service and the generic field social workers except through personal CPN contact. A specialist hospital-based social worker post is vacant. One of the specialist CPNs does, however, have an excellent personal relationship with the OIC of Welland House, a large new Part III home where a purpose-built specialist unit has been established on the lines of Flat Two in Orchard House (see page 104).

Psychologist
As in South Cambridgeshire (see page 116) a psychologist is jointly funded by the NHS and SSD but has relatively little contact with Dove House.

Physiotherapy
In addition to joining the day centre OT aide for weekly music and movement in Dove House, a physiotherapist uses two half-sessions to give advice to Dove House staff about individual patients.

Summary
A visit to Dove House generates mixed feelings of admiration and disappointment. On the one hand this is a pioneering unit which was well ahead of its time in seeking to provide an autonomous 'domestic' longstay unit within the NHS. The extent to which this has been achieved, largely through the vision and determination of Willie Kwa, is remarkable. On the other hand, the furnishing and decoration come nowhere near matching good SSD standards, and the quality of care though good, is not as exceptional as the official level of staffing and the existence of the nearby day hospital would seem to make possible. Dove House appears to be struggling to maintain its philosophy and its relative autonomy in the face, if not of deliberate opposition, of a system of administration and resource allocation which finds it difficult to accept and encompass aberrations of this kind. A visit leaves one with serious doubts as to whether it is possible for the NHS, as currently constituted, to provide specialist care units in which staff can forget that they are part of a hospital-dominated service and provide genuinely homely care.

THE BUNGALOW
Honiton Hospital, Marlpitts Road, Honiton, Devon: Tel–0404 44511

Principal characteristics
The Bungalow is a new, purpose-built unit intended to be a focal point for the provision of services for confused elderly people in the Honiton and Ottery St Mary localities. It offers 20 beds and associated facilities for longstay, relief and care assessment, together with ample space for day care and treatment. However, the emphasis is on the provision of a 'service' rather than 'beds', and the staff are strongly committed to providing care and support in people's own homes. It is the first of ten services which are planned to replace a traditional psychiatric hospital at Exminster, and the unit had only just been opened when it was visited. It is, however, of great importance as a pioneer example of the successful transfer of resources from traditional psychiatric care and re-thinking the mode of health service provision for this client group. (Similar plans are being made for acute psychiatry and mental handicap.)

History
A great deal of time and trouble has been taken to work through the procedure of hospital closure and the transfer of staff and patients. A detailed policy document (District Procedure No 17) was agreed with the trades unions concerned which guaranteed that there would be no compulsory redundancies. A commitment was also made to staff to give 'every encouragement and assistance to develop new styles of service'. This commitment included: a right to initial interview with a head of department to ascertain staff aspirations; an offer of transfer with the ward concerned; the right to an interview for other vacancies; and a generous definition of 'comparable' posts. In return employees were asked to accept: much greater flexibility in terms of attachment to a mental health service rather than a ward; abolition of day and night nursing appointments; a willingness to work in the community if required; and the designation of domestic staff as nursing auxiliaries with management by the charge nurse.

It proved to be particularly important for senior nurses to know their place in the new system 'otherwise you have people with a vested interest in maintaining the status quo'. The senior nurses then needed to help the designated charge nurses to work through the new concepts of service provision with their 'shadow teams'. Parallel to this process was the selection of patients for the new units. This required a census of hospital patients suffering from organic disorders which identified them in terms of age, sex, consultant, diagnosis, area of origin, area where their visitors lived, and frequency of visiting, so that patients could be transferred to a situation where they would be nearest home and most in contact with their families. In spite of the care taken to work out procedures and fit appointments to personal circumstances the process took a long time and The Bungalow, which was the first completed unit, opened eight months later than had been planned. (Subsequent units are on target.) The delay may have been occasioned not only by the complex practical details which had to be sorted out, but also by the need to work through the loss of the old hospital where some staff families have worked for generations. One informant compared the situation to a coalmine closure.

While all this was going on, a great deal of effort was being made to build up local participation in the decentralisation process, and local planning teams and relative support groups were developed. These measures generated enthusiastic local support for the scheme and still provide a solid base for an investigation of local need and development of local services (see below). When the building was nearly ready, both staff and prospective patients visited it to work out exactly how it would be used and to become familiar with it. Final commissioning in August 1985 was therefore the culmination of a very long process, but the procedures developed and lessons learned have made similar developments in other parts of the health district much quicker.

Design and furnishing
The Bungalow is one of eight standard units originally planned at a cost of around £450,000 each, though two of these have now been shelved in favour of active, multi-disciplinary domiciliary teams. The standard unit was conceived with the aim of creating a homely environment which also offered maximum flexibility so that the accommodation could be altered in response to the demands of the locality—for example by reducing the sleeping area and expanding space available for day care. In this instance, however, the internal layout is on traditional hospital lines with four four-bedded wards, and four single rooms arranged on each

side of a central passage, which takes a right-angled turn half-way down. A nursing station on the corner enables maximum surveillance. A large open-plan sitting/dining room, partitioned by room dividers, is situated in the angle of the passage, with an adjoining small sitting room intended for groups and quiet use. A large room on the other side of the passage will be primarily occupied by day attenders. There are two bathrooms with WCs and four other WCs. An office, interview room and staff changing room are situated at one end of the passage. Furniture and fittings are of a very high quality, but it is a pity that four-bedded rooms have been retained. These are divided into bays which do not offer much space to wash and dress patients, and the overall impression is still strongly that of a hospital ward.

Ability range of residents
The thirteen longstay patients who were being cared for in The Bungalow at the time of the visit had an average score of 9.4 on the CRBRS Scale with eight scoring 10 or 11. They had been transferred from Exminster. The level of dependency is therefore still very high at present, though it was reported that there had been a noticeable improvement since the move. The level of physical dependency is also high and one male patient who has suffered a stroke is violently resistive to receiving any assistance. However, two recent admissions scored only 6 on the scale and, as the service is intended to provide treatment and support for the whole range of organic brain failure and not just severe dementia, it seems likely that as time goes on the nature of the in-patient group will change considerably.

Philosophy
The aims of the charge nurse, as set down in the job description are:

a) to establish, develop and promote an individualised and enlightened philosophy of nursing care, embracing the physical, psychological and spiritual needs of the elderly mentally infirm;

b) to lead and inspire an on-going purposeful philosophy of reality-orientated nursing care throughout the unit;

c) to facilitate, nurture and energise support relationships with individuals and voluntary groups involved in the care of the elderly mentally infirm and their supporters;

d) to strive to develop ever higher levels of excellence in the provision of orientated care to the elderly mentally infirm users of the service.

The senior nurse in the Mental Health District is responsible both for formulating these high ideals and for integrating old and new staff members and making the philosophy work. He sees the key concept as commitment to providing 'a service', 'not just beds' and to making the individual care plan and key worker system a reality. Longstay care, shortstay care, day care and community care must, he believes, be held in a balance with maximum emphasis on flexibility of staff roles (including inter-changeability of domestic and nursing tasks) and delegation of responsibility and openness in the decision-making process. The 'elderly team' which meets fortnightly (see below) should act as the gatekeeper to all resources, including long-term beds, and should be open to everyone who feels they have business there.

Staffing
Staff levels
Because of the procedures required by the closure of Exminster Hospital, The Bungalow was not fully staffed at the time of the initial visit. The varied nature of the job had, however, attracted a lot of interest and there had been no difficulty in recruiting well-qualified staff nurses, some of whom had come from a different part of England (there has however been difficulty in keeping them). Day staff allocation for the 20 in-patient beds (excluding the charge nurse) is four SRNs, four SENs and six nursing assistants, giving a total of 28 hours per patient week. Two SRNs and four nursing assistants are allocated for night coverage, though all staff rotate through the 24 hours. A further charge nurse and staff nurse and two nursing assistants are allocated for day patients and community involvement. In addition, there is a weekly allocation for two physiotherapy sessions, six hours senior OT time, 42 hours basic grade OT time, three psychology sessions, and half a day from the pharmacist. None of these provisions, except the pharmacy time, were in operation at the time of the visit.

Nursing staff on shifts work from 7.45 am to 4.15 pm, 12.45 pm to 9.15 pm and 9 pm to 8 am. The system thus gives an overlap during the middle of the day which should allow for one-to-one activity and staff meetings. It is worthy of mention that a full-time ward clerk is employed (in stark contrast to the lack of clerical help in local authority homes).

Staff qualifications and training
Professional qualifications are noted above. Training within the

staff team had not had time to settle down to a pattern at the time of the visit, though it is clear from the job descriptions that a continued teaching and learning process is envisaged. What is exceptional is the effort which has been made by the Elderly Training Team of the Exeter HA to encourage grass roots service providers—such as home helps, auxiliary nurses and sheltered housing wardens—to think through their concepts of 'confusion' and arrive at a common understanding of good service provision. The Authority runs inter-disciplinary training days which begin by using 'normalisation' training techniques to encourage attenders to identify practices to which elderly people are subjected and which they would dislike for themselves. The day goes on to give information about the differential diagnoses of confusion; factors which exacerbate it; and issues of management, assessment and communication. Trained staff are used to present the sessions, which has the effect of making them clarify their own attitudes to the issues raised. These meetings are seen both as a 'consciousness-raising exercise' and a 'public relations exercise'. It is hoped that they will encourage the integration of the new psychogeriatric units within current service provision, and give a taste for joint training, and that it will be possible to follow them up with a more structured package. Such a package may be integrated with training for student nurses in the dispersed units and with training for SSD staff. The Elderly Training Team, in which a psychologist plays an important role, is also involved in a training course for middle management in domiciliary, residential, day care and nursing roles to introduce them to 'normalisation' concepts (see page 166). The audiences for both these training programmes are people concerned specifically with mental dependency in old age rather than with all client groups, but their similarity with those envisaged in Stockport (page 133) is worth noting. Here, however, we have the HA going into the social services field, while in Stockport a reverse movement is hoped for.

Staff communication
Here again, the system had not settled down sufficiently at the time of the visit for a clear pattern to have emerged. The plan is to divide The Bungalow staff into two teams—'red' and 'blue'—each led by a staff nurse who is regarded as the key worker. He or she will work in co-operation with one of the team who is the 'co-worker' with responsibility for a particular patient. Responsibility will include assessment, record-keeping and on-going monitoring, using the 'traffic light' recording system (see below).

The job description of the charge nurse requires the post holder to 'exercise leadership and energise staff morale through the organisation of a communications system within the unit that is both accessible and sensitive in allowing the exchange of ideas and information across all levels'.

Regime
Getting up and going to bed
The staff on night duty start getting the patients up during the last hour of their shift and on the day of the visit about half were up by 8 am. Everyone was up by the time breakfast was served at about 8.45 am. The process seemed relaxed and some patients were not dressed until after breakfast because it was intended to bath them then. Going to bed is also gradual with about five patients still up at 10 pm.

Meals
A well-cooked, varied and generous menu is available from the Honiton Hospital kitchen with a full cooked breakfast and two course lunch and supper—the latter, served at 6 pm, was one of the latest main meals noted in this study. Meals are served on round polished wooden tables, with patients sitting four to a table on comfortable chairs with arms. They are grouped according to relationships and eating ability. The staff take an unusual amount of trouble to offer choice and to get a response to the offer, and they are encouraged to eat surplus food themselves while sitting with the patients since this is thought to provide a good 'role model' for table manners.

Activities
An effort had just begun to get a music and movement session going on a regular basis, and this had elicited a considerable response from patients. It is hoped that properly organised and regular activity will follow the appointment of an OT and the arrival of shortstay and day patients. However, one informant expressed concern that a basic grade OT was too inexperienced for work of this difficulty, especially if she were appointed when the routine of the unit had become established, and that there was a danger that she would simply become 'an extra pair of hands'. There had not been time for other activities to become routine and, although staff have clearly been encouraged to talk to patients, their efforts are not always very appropriate in terms of reality orientation. For example, a patient who complained of being cold while she was being dressed was asked 'is it

snowing?' (on a wet day in early September) and another who was taking her time about the process was told 'you are procrastinating'.

Bathing
Baths are given according to need under the direction of the key worker.

Management of continence
By day: The HA has provided a gadget which is supposed to clean the cloth-upholstered chairs without leaving any smell, but staff were not confident about its efficacy and incontinence sheets on the chairs were in general use. Similarly, there was concern about the practicability of carpeting the lounge floor in Flotex: 'it is stained already'.

By night: In contrast to the practice in Exminster Hospital, routine toileting and the '2 am check and change' no longer take place. Again staff are unhappy about this, complaining that patients are very wet in the morning and that the Kylie sheets in use, which cost £16 each, were not washed according to the manufacturer's instructions by the hospital laundry and came back 'a foot square'. 'Attends' pads are now in use at night, but when these become wet they tend to fall down round the ankles and are then dangerous if the patient tries to walk. A pad combined with elasticated briefs would, it was felt, be preferable. In general, the staff on night duty were said to feel uncomfortable because 'they were not doing enough for their patients'.

Reviews
Patients are reviewed on a weekly basis by the use of the 'traffic light' system. This involves filling a small circle with a green, yellow or red colour depending on whether the patient is minimally, moderately or severely limited in a range of 23 physical and social tasks and skills. Six columns of such circles are printed on one sheet so change in a particular ability over a period, whether positive or negative, is quickly perceived and appropriate steps can be taken to encourage or limit the alteration. The key worker is responsible for seeing that these sheets are completed in consultation with the co-worker concerned.

Involvement with relatives
As was noted above, every attempt has been made to involve relatives with the development of The Bungalow, and free visiting

is encouraged. Those spoken to were delighted with the contrast to Exminster, but the development of mutually supportive relationships will take time and will be related to the development of day care, respite care and community care services.

Assessment and admission procedures

A small multi-disciplinary group called 'The Elderly Team' normally includes a psychogeriatrician, SSD social worker, community psychiatric nurse, charge nurse of The Bungalow and psychologist, but may be open to other people with relevant interests (see below). It meets fortnightly to consider: referrals; allocation of responsibility to follow them up; plans for further management (including admission on a day or residential basis for assessment); and admission for respite care and longstay care. At the time of the visit the system was in its infancy, but there were indications that it would take time to establish the acceptance of The Bungalow's own staff as community care providers and to ensure that final decision-making did not automatically lie with the doctor.

Once someone is admitted, a detailed 'Patient's Profile Recording Form' is, or should be, completed. The last three pages of this covers fairly standard items of physical and mental state, and capacity for self care, but the first two pages record aspects of family relationships and previous personality which are not often found in hospital notes. They were derived from a schedule devised by Glenda Watt at the Royal Edinburgh Hospital. After completion of the initial assessment, the progress of the patient is monitored by the use of the 'traffic light' chart described above.

Professional support services

The emphasis is what The Bungalow and its staff, working in the context of the local Mental Health Team, can offer the community, rather than vice versa. Preparation for setting up the unit (as for all the units envisaged under the decentralising process) has included the setting up of a locality management structure. This consists of local people who are leaders in the community. In the case of Honiton, it includes a GP, a head teacher, an officer in the local police force, a clergymen and a pharmacist. Membership of these teams is by invitation, based on local information, and an effort is made to have a reasonably small but well-balanced representation. They help to define needs, plan services, monitor provision and tap community resources.

More detailed data relating to the elderly is being obtained by a 'census' which identifies people known or thought to be 'confused' by GPs and other providers of health and social services; 149 such people were identified in the Honiton and Ottery St Mary localities. The census 'provides a surface appreciation of local need in terms of the potential demand on services for elderly confused persons and where the demands may possibly arise from (ie in the community, private residential/nursing homes etc)'. To make a more specific assessment of the needs of the people affected and their carers, a further in-depth series of interviews with a sample of the households identified is being carried out. This will seek to evaluate the quality of, and gaps in, present service provision and make it possible to develop a conceptual model of what a service should provide. The whole emphasis is thus on finding out what the service should be doing rather than setting one up on a preconceived model.

The Bungalow works very closely with the CPNs, social workers and other staff based in the local Mental Health Team office, and the charge nurse works to the senior nurse belonging to this team. As was noted above, the general policy is to emphasise that The Bungalow is there to provide services rather than beds, including very flexible community care and day care.

Medical support
Ordinary medical cover is supplied by a GP based in the nearby health centre who takes a great interest in The Bungalow and its patients. The facilities of the community hospital are also available. However, at the time of the visit the role of the responsible consultant psychogeriatrician had yet to be determined as she was sick when the unit was commissioned, and the clinical registrar who was standing in for her was not in a position to take binding decisions on her behalf. There would seem to be major issues about decision-making to be worked out in relation to the respective responsibilities of the psychiatrist and the Elderly Planning Team as a whole.

Social services
A field worker is involved in the Elderly Planning Team and there is good local liaison with home help organisers and other SSD personnel. At a more senior level, joint consultation is taking place about the future role of the two specialist EMI homes in the area and their relationship to The Bungalow and its staff.

Summary
As The Bungalow was visited only one month after it opened, it was too early to gain a clear idea of its success in reaching its objectives. The whole exercise has been, as the community general manager says, a 'quantum leap' from the traditional bed-focused care provided at Exminster Hospital and there is inevitably a long way to go before local needs are fully identified, the service settled down to meet them and the staff retrained. However, The Bungalow does provide proof that the NHS can generate effective alternatives to traditional modes of care and that these can be run on a cost-effective basis. It will be extremely interesting to see how this pioneer project develops.

SEPTEMBER WARD
York House (Specialist ESMI Unit), Royal
Infirmary, Oxford Road, Manchester 3:
Tel–061 276 1234

Principal characteristics
September Ward is the longstay 28-bedded ward in a purpose-
built unit within the sprawling Manchester Royal Infirmary
teaching hospital. An assessment/treatment ward (mainly for
organic illness) and very large and well-staffed day hospital are
provided on the same site. It was intended that the ward should
benefit from the availability of a wide range of professional skills
and sophisticated physical treatment facilities combined with
high ideals in the provision of care. In fact the ward is fairly
traditional both in design and regime. The difficulty experienced
in matching ideals to practice, and the advantages and disadvantages of providing long-term care on the same site as other forms
of treatment, are the main points of interest.

History
There was no specialist psychogeriatric service in Central Manchester until 1982 when three community psychiatric nurses and
a specialist social worker were appointed to work under the
direction of Dr Jolley, a psychogeriatrician based in South
Manchester (the Withington Hospital). The emphasis was therefore on the provision of community support until, largely through
Dr Jolley's efforts, the present purpose-built unit was opened in
June 1984.

In spite of the unit's existence this emphasis has been retained.
The two consultants spend a great deal of time making their
skills and knowledge available to field and residential social
services personnel, district nurses and wardens in sheltered
housing. The community psychiatric nurses are community-
based and operate an open referral system, and they each have
responsibility for maintaining liaison with four or five residential
homes. The opening of the ESMI unit gave rise to some unrealistic
expectations that henceforth everyone suffering from dementia
would be cared for in hospital, and a lot of time and effort was
needed to clarify the unit's role, especially in relation to its very
limited capacity to provide longstay care. This was further

restricted, as far as admitting patients from the community was concerned, because it had always been intended that September Ward should start by taking patients who were currently receiving care at Prestwich psychiatric hospital and who had been admitted from a Central Manchester address within the last ten years. These patients were collected at Prestwich and lived together for a year before the transfer. Great care was taken over this with staff from York House spending some time with the proposed patients at Prestwich and taking them to visit the new ward. They were admitted in twos over a period of a week in June 1984, together with two patients from the Withington Hospital. (At the time of the visit in August 1985 seven of the original patients were still living.) Owing to staffing difficulties the original patients were mixed with longstay and assessment patients on October Ward for the first month and then separated out. By August 1985 18 beds on September Ward were in use, though only 15 were filled on the day of the visit. The remaining ten beds were empty because of staffing difficulties. There was therefore much more space available than would normally have been the case.

Philosophy
The senior nurse responsible for commissioning the ESMI unit has high ideals of maintaining capacity for self care in this client group and has produced an assessment guide which encourages a very detailed analysis of individual patient's capacity over a whole range of activity including: ability to maintain a safe environment; communication; breathing; eating and drinking; personal cleaning and dressing; elimination; maintaining body temperature; mobility; maintenance of self esteem and dignity; expression of sexuality; social and occupational activities; sleep; and support in the dying process. It also asks the nurse to describe the patient's behavioural excesses and deficits; the events and objects which motivate, sustain, reinforce and terminate behaviour; the degree of insight, self-control and awareness exercised by the patient; and the patient's personality attributes, skills and interests.

This guide is reflected in the job description of staff nurses in the unit which includes responsibility 'in conjunction with other nursing team members to assess, plan, implement, and evaluate care to help patients attain the maximum level of independence, dignity and happiness while maintaining the optimum contact with reality as is compatible with their acquired pathology'.

Design and furnishing

York House is a standard North West Regional HA ESMI unit
built on three floors, double-glazed throughout and modernistic
in appearance with a profusion of bright blue and bright
red paint. The ground floor is mainly used for a very generously
planned day hospital and staff offices, with September Ward on
the first floor and October Ward above it. Entrance to September
Ward is effected by simultaneously pressing a button and turning
a door handle, and exit is by punching a numbered pad in correct
sequence. A wide passage leads into a centrally-sited and very
large day room/dining room, dominated by a nursing station
reminiscent of a very long hotel bar. (This is virtually unused.)
Two six-bedded wards, each with its own WC and two wash
basins, are situated on each side of the day room, and four single
rooms lead off the day room behind the nursing station. Apart
from the plumbing in the wards there are three bathrooms with
en suite WCs, a shower, a medi-bath and three separate WCs,
two of which open off the day room. An additional smaller lounge
at the far end of the passage seems to be little used, except by
staff groups. There is a kitchenette for preparing breakfast and
hot drinks. An enclosed garden is available but since September
Ward is on the first floor it is not accessible to unaccompanied
patients. The day room is carpeted in a pleasant light green and
chairs are arranged in small groups round low tables. Most are
fairly standard in design but three Kirton chairs (see page 67)
have been provided. Dining chairs are padded and reasonably
comfortable. All other floors have a hard and shiny surface.
Overall, in spite of the high quality finish and furnishing, the
effect is clinical and impersonal, though an attempt has been
made to individualise the ward cubicles.

Ability range of residents

The average CRBRS score for the fifteen patients in the ward at
the time of the visit was 8.5 with a range of 5–11. One patient
scored 11, and seven scored 10, so that over half the ward were
reckoned to be totally without memory or communication.
However, several had difficulty with speech which may have made
their level of dementia appear worse than it was. Several residents
required assistance with walking and four needed physical help
with feeding, but no-one was totally chair-bound. Two or three
patients were thought to be potentially suitable for residential
care if a place could be found, and the one patient, who scored 5
on the CRBRS scale, was later transferred to a Part III home.
Particular behaviour problems included regular or intermittent

shouting, interference with other people's food, resistance to washing and dressing and undressing, and removal of clothing.

Staffing
Staff levels
Staffing is unusual in that four charge nurses share responsibility for the ward during the day. This is said to be advantageous because it is easier to recruit charge nurses than staff nurses; it ensures that someone with full clinical experience is on the ward at all times; and it prevents any one person from being snowed under with administrative chores. However, the system seems to have major drawbacks in that no one person has a full sense of responsibility and leadership. At 25.6 nursing hours per resident week, staffing levels are similar to The Bungalow though lower than Dove House. When the ward is fully staffed and has its full complement of 28 patients it should be provided with four charge nurses, four staff nurses, five enrolled nurses and 10.5 auxiliaries. It also has access, in theory, to the specialist skills of a physiotherapist, clinical psychologist, speech therapist and occupational therapist. In practice, however, as is noted below, these practitioners are based in the day centre, and September Ward patients only see them if they are brought down for particular activities which are thought to be appropriate, or if their advice is asked about a particular patient. Usual shifts are 7.30 am to 3.30 pm; 1 pm to 9 pm and 8.45 pm to 7.45 am. Most of the junior staff rotate through the shifts, including night duty, and there is one charge nurse responsible for the night staff on both wards. It has proved difficult to recruit suitably trained staff to work on this ward and there is a high turnover. This may be due to the current policy of recruiting staff specifically to work on the longstay ward so there is no possibility of a work programme which includes some time with less disabled people. Also there is competition for trained staff since an increasing number of specialist units are being opened without closing traditional psychiatric hospitals. Further difficulties in recruitment are expected with the ending of SEN training, but it is hoped to remedy the situation by getting the whole psychiatric section recognised for RMN training. High quality, untrained, staff are plentiful.

Staff qualifications and training
A careful induction training course was carried out before the unit opened, but staff turnover has meant that many of those now working there have not experienced this and the original ideals have rather been lost. At the time of the visit it was planned to

close the day hospital for a day and review the operation of the unit as a whole with a view to setting new goals. Nursing staff from the wards were to be represented at this meeting. Occasional unit-based seminars are held on particular subjects, such as feeding or communication, and these meetings are open to any staff who wish to attend including ward orderlies. (Ward orderlies, who are employed in place of 'domestics', are encouraged to see themselves as part of the care staff, but privatisation may destroy this approach.) New auxiliary nurses receive one week basic induction training before they start on the ward and it is planned to give them a programme of ward-based lectures on specific subjects and a two-month attachment, on a rota basis, to therapist staff in the day hospital, so that they can come back to the wards and practise the skills they have learned. The hospital also has a lively programme of in-service training for qualified staff.

Staff communication
A weekly, multi-disciplinary ward round is attended by the consultant, registrar (a trainee psychiatrist), physiotherapist, occupational therapist and speech therapist, but only by the senior nurse on duty so the opportunity to use this period as a means of staff training seems to be lost. Otherwise the only meetings regularly held at ward level are formal handover sessions. Senior staff in the various professions meet to plan the work of the unit as a whole.

Regime
Getting up and going to bed
No-one was up before the morning handover session at 7.30 am (one person who tried to get up was encouraged to go back to sleep), though all but one patient were up and dressed by breakfast time at 8.45 am. (The one exception needed physical treatment which would have involved undressing her again and it was felt that there was no point in disturbing her.) Patients who have had a bad night are encouraged to sleep late. The getting up procedure seemed to be relaxed and easy. Cubicle curtains were drawn and privacy was maintained. As far as possible dressing was done by members of the same team each day (see below). Two patients went to bed before the night staff came on at 9 pm—one because she was tired and the other because she had developed pressure sores from too much sitting. Patients were asked if they wanted to go to bed and the process was gradual but everyone was in bed by 10.30 pm

Meals

Breakfast consisted of cereal or porridge, the latter is brought to the ward and kept hot in the kitchenette. Sandwiches, orange juice and tea are prepared by ward orderlies in the kitchenette. Breakfast can be served at any time and is a popular meal because people are hungry. One man who likes porridge sometimes has several helpings and makes it the main meal of the day. For other meals trolleys are brought onto the ward from the main hospital kitchen and plated meals dished out. There is some adjustment to the needs of patients—for example some had soup served in cups rather than bowls because they found this easier to cope with, and some had sandwiches rather than a cooked meal because they preferred this and would not eat cooked food. Reinforced drinks are used to supplement diet if not enough is being eaten. Four of the least impaired patients had knives and forks laid and sat at their own table—others were separated according to disability, need for help and anti-social habits. At least three patients needed feeding. A man who was asleep at dinner time and was said to be aggressive if he was woken up, was allowed to sleep on. Staff said they thought the food tended to be unimaginative, too heavy for elderly people and was often too tough to be chewed without teeth. They also expressed dislike of repetitive 'slop' and milk puddings. Negotiations are under way to have a light 'snack' meal served at midday. Meal times are at approximately 8.30 am, 12 noon and 5 pm but these may be later if arrival of the food trolley is delayed and patients may spend quite a long time sitting waiting for their meal at the table as a result.

Activities

Each patient is given a most detailed assessment of their capacity to perform daily living activities and this is intended to be used as a basis for teaching, guiding, and 'providing a developmental and therapeutic environment' for the patient. Using the assessment, a care plan is drawn up for each patient—sometimes with advice from the OT, speech therapist or physiotherapist—on means of dealing with particular problems of mobility, eating, communication, dressing and so on, as well as the usual personal details and medical assessment on admission. In practice, however, the goals specified in the care plan tend to become stereotyped—for example, 'the patient will become more continent' or 'the patient will be less aggressive'—and it has proved difficult in the face of severe chronic disability to maintain any real sense of consistent effort to make the care plans a reality.

When time is available staff try to engage patients in one-to-one activity on the ward—looking at magazines, encouraging writing, talking and cuddling—and the team system is meant to encourage this. There has also been an attempt by one of the staff nurses to start an RO group, but nursing staff shortages have made it very difficult to maintain any activities on a regular basis, and there is at present no formal OT involvement on the ward. In general the day hospital staff are reluctant to accept September Ward patients (unless they are accompanied by staff on a one-to-one basis) because they are too disruptive and demanding of staff time. The ward can seldom afford staff for this purpose, except on a Friday afternoon when about half the patients go down for a social and singsong. Records of familiar tunes are played in the ward but this tends to become a background noise rather than a focus of attention. Provision of activity will, it is hoped, improve when staff have some OT experience (see above). Similarly September Ward patients have little involvement in day hospital physiotherapy as it is considered to be too disorienting for them to be brought down for this, and there is not yet sufficient staff for a physiotherapist to work regularly on the ward.

Clothing
Clothing is bought personally—if possible by taking the patients to the shops, but otherwise by taking measurements and ordering via the hospital system, or buying on behalf of patients. Clothing is repaired and laundered within the unit (three laundry assistants are employed). People are encouraged to maintain previous styles of dress, even if these appear eccentric. One male patient for instance prefers to wear red golfing trousers. Choice of what to put on is offered when patients are being dressed. Night clothes, however, are provided from communal stock.

Bathing
In theory the staff are divided into three nursing teams each of which take responsibility for providing personal care to a group of patients on the basis of individual need. In practice, however, staff shortages make it difficult to maintain the team system and patients are usually bathed by the staff available in the afternoon when a double shift is on duty.

Management of continence
By day: Incontinence charts are kept for all patients and an effort is made to assist them according to individual need. In practice however it is very difficult to prevent this from becoming a

toiletting round at the usual times. Incontinence pads are used if necessary.

By night: Commodes are used as little as possible as each ward has a lavatory and WCs are close to the side rooms. As in the daytime an attempt is made to look after patients according to individual need based on observation rather than a generalised routine. Kylie sheets are not used.

Reviews
In theory the care plan is reviewed every two months but, judging by the records, this is difficult to maintain and is in any case little more than a formality. Otherwise there is a routine handover session and a weekly ward round which, as was noted above, is attended by representatives of the various disciplines but not by nursing staff (except for the senior nurse on duty).

Personal allowance
This is banked with the patients' services officer who is co-operative in enabling cash to be withdrawn on demand for shopping and other personal expenses. As well as buying clothing, personal money is used to buy non-institutional towels and will be used to provide personal bedspreads and aprons for use at meals. One patient has a nightcap of brandy instead of medication but it was not ascertained whether this had been bought with his own money.

Outings
Visits to stately homes, Blackpool lights and so on, take place from time to time using the hospital minibus, but these excursions are limited by lack of staff and difficulty in finding a staff member who is qualified to drive. Staff also take patients out on an individual basis, for example to the shops and pub, but again staff shortages makes it difficult to do this with any frequency.

Involvement with relatives
A relatives' group is held once a month in the afternoon for relatives of patients in both September and October wards, the venue being the small lounge on September Ward. Numbers have varied from one to eleven and transport is provided by a social worker if necessary. It is run by the OT along with September Ward nursing staff, and is on a very unstructured basis which allows members to select the subjects raised. Talk ranges from the weather and transport problems to guilt and

grief. The group was once used to ventilate hostility about the lack of help one supporter had experienced (this was due to an unco-operative GP rather than lack of psychogeriatric facilities) but in general it is felt that relatives 'are too grateful' and 'praise too much'. Some maintain contact for some time after the patient's death. Several pictures in the September Ward passage have been donated by relatives in memory of deceased patients, and brass plaques record this fact.

Volunteers
No volunteers were used on the ward at the time of the visit.

Assessment and admission procedures
Admission is by the decision of the psychiatrist, after assessment in October Ward or the day hospital, or after long-term contact while still living at home. Ward staff are not involved in the decision, though during the visit they successfully resisted a new admission because of staff shortages.

Professional support services
The presence of the day hospital means that excellent specialist advice can be obtained from a psychologist, occupational therapist, physiotherapist and (which is probably a unique provision) a full-time speech therapist but, as has already been mentioned, none of these professionals has any routine involvement with the Ward. A joint psychiatric/geriatric clinic allows easy referral for help with physical health problems, and the facilities of a sophisticated teaching hospital mean that neurological or other investigations can be easily undertaken.

Summary
September Ward was opened with the highest possible objectives of providing care which maintained dignity and independence. The ideals are still there but the practice has been blunted by difficulties in staff recruitment, the institutional and clinical ward layout, pressures on senior staff and a seemingly inescapable human tendency to put most effort and available resources into the sectors which are likely to be most rewarding.

It is not yet clear how far these are teething problems which will be resolved when the unit becomes settled and fully-staffed, but it seems only too likely that the pressure of numbers in a fully-occupied, 28-bedded ward will outweigh any potential improvements. Already staff talk about the difficulty of combating institutionalised treatment when dealing with patients, and the advantages of much smaller groups on a 'villa' principle. September Ward has everything going for it, both in the idealism and enthusiasm of those who set it up and in investment in modern plant and skilled ancillary support. If it cannot, in the long run, offer longstay care which is manifestly of a higher quality than that provided in other environments, the justification for providing longstay care in this type of setting needs serious debate.

ETTRICK WARD, DINGLETON HOSPITAL
Melrose, Roxburghshire, Scotland TD6 9HN:
Tel–Melrose 2727

Principal characteristics

Dingleton was opened in 1872 as a traditional psychiatric hospital in the Scottish Borders serving a geographically extensive rural catchment area of 100,000 people. Nearly half of its 336 beds are psychogeriatric, but it also offers acute and long-term psychiatric and mental handicap services. One of its psychiatric wards has been included in this study in order to compare the care given in a traditional psychiatric hospital with that provided in smaller institutions. Dingleton seemed particularly suitable for this purpose because it has a national and international reputation as the pioneer of the 'therapeutic community' model of management (discussed below) and because of its extensive use of hospital-based nursing staff to provide crisis intervention and continuing care in the community. It seemed that if there is a viable role for traditional psychiatric hospitals in the field of longstay psychogeriatric care, Dingleton would be able to show what it is. One ward has been made the main focus of the case study, but its operation cannot be understood without setting it in a wider context.

History

Dingleton originally became famous in 1949 as the first psychiatric hospital to 'open its doors', and again in the 1960s when its physician superintendent, Dr Maxwell Jones, based his regime on a concept of social psychiatry which requires patients to take as much responsibility for themselves and their surroundings as they can effectively manage. In order to make this a reality, the same responsibility has to be given to the staff.

The consequence is that the authority structure is 'flattened' with both staff and patients sharing in decision-making through a whole range of meetings, and patients are actively involved in the day-to-day work of running the wards as part of the treatment process—hence the term 'therapeutic community'. Outside the hospital, a multi-disciplinary hospital-based team takes responsibility for all psychiatric referrals in one section of the catchment area, and also covers one speciality (mental handicap, 'rehabilitation' or psychogeriatrics) for the whole area. All hospital staff are committed to treating people in their own homes if this is possible rather than bringing them in to the often far-distant hospital.

Although this regime has been established for so long, it was some time before it was applied to psychogeriatrics. Previously elderly patients were mixed together indiscriminately in huge wards, and, along with the staff who looked after them, were largely untouched by the therapeutic community concept. It was not until 1972 that an attempt was made to involve all ward staff in the caring role and minimise routine and maximise activity. Patients with roughly comparable diagnoses and levels of disability were put together with the intention of moving them to another ward if their level of dependency increased. Six wards were set up to implement this policy, giving each maximum freedom to develop its own ethos:

Traquair—a 24-bedded assessment/relief/respite ward was, at the time of the visit, largely 'silted up' with people awaiting longstay care. This ward has an independent entrance and relatively domestic-scale accommodation. There is much emphasis on physiotherapy, retraining in self care, reality orientation and daily living skills.

Glentress—provides 34 beds for the least dependent longstay patients, most of whom are 'graduates' or functionally ill. It also provides day care and relief admission. Lounge space has been subdivided as much as possible by the use of room dividers, ornaments and plants, and one five-bedded ward and associated sitting room has been set up for an 'independent group' who, with assistance, do their own cooking, cleaning and shopping and could move out into a group home if staff cover could be provided. The charge nurse here puts primary emphasis on external activities such as shopping, encouragement of self care, and maintenance of existing skills and interests.

Eddleston Ward—patients on this 23-bedded, upgraded ward have dementia, but retain some capacity for self care and verbal interaction, and this is reinforced by encouraging communication in small groups and by regular use of a separate day centre some distance from the ward (see below). Imaginative use is made of video equipment to encourage reminiscence and staff training.

Bowmont Ward—caters for 30 severely demented patients and

has recently been upgraded by providing two sitting rooms, so that disturbed patients can be separated from the rest, and smaller sleeping areas. Its appearance is, however, still very clinical and layout is awkward and confusing. At the time of the visit it had only just been recommissioned and further assessment was not possible.

Ettrick Ward—this 30-bedded ward caters for the same level of dependency as Bowmont and is described in more detail below.

Teviot Ward—is an attractive 20-bedded unit with French doors opening onto a garden and it caters for 20 elderly women who need continuous physical nursing care.

This system is still working well, given the major problems inherent in the hospital building and a huge catchment area, but it has also run into difficulties. Pressure of demand has meant that the shortstay ward is largely blocked with patients awaiting longstay care; lack of community-based facilities means that patients who are suitable for discharge have nowhere to go; and lack of vacancies in the high-dependency wards and pressure from the community means that patients cannot be moved on. Even if a place is available staff are often reluctant to lose 'their' patients unless caring for them has become impossible. The lack of provision for male patients in Teviot Ward also means that very physically dependent men have to stay in Bowmont or Ettrick. More fundamentally, there is some sense of unease about the quality and future of the service. There is inevitably a clash of priorities between acute psychiatry and psychogeriatrics within the hospital, and between psychiatry and the needs of a new DGH which makes considerable demands on available resources. There are plans to develop a proper community-based service with local units providing domiciliary support, day care, respite care and longstay beds, but progress on the establishment of these is slow because of pressure on resources. Nonetheless, three community resource day centres for psychogeriatrics have been established and are proving most valuable. Also a temporary transfer of Glentress Ward to a recently vacated local authority home in Galashiels while the ward was being refurbished, has proved the viability of community-based longstay care. The psychogeriatric team is longing to take much more of their work outside the hospital, but cannot do so. It is in the light of these aspirations and these frustrations that the rest of the description must be read.

Design and furnishing
Ettrick is a 30-bed, mixed sex ward on a semi-basement level.
The windows of the day room look out onto a sunken area which,
though filled with greenery, has a restricted outlook. Electric
lighting is needed almost all day in winter. The day room itself
is very large with chairs arranged round the edge and backing
onto a pillar in the centre. A glassed-wall office serves as a divider
between the day room and the dining room and pantry. The day
room is separated from the sleeping area by a corridor, some
130 feet long and six feet wide, which runs the whole length of
the unit. The male and female sections of the sleeping area are
partially separated by a clothes store which juts out into the room,
and one side of this has been covered by a life-size photograph
of a wood in autumn. Bright window curtains, cubicle curtains
and bedspreads help to relieve an essentially unattractive area,
and the cubicle curtains are not only available but used.

Ability range of residents
The average on the CRBRS scale is 8.5 with nearly half (13) of
the 28 patients scoring 10 or 11. Levels of physical disability are
high, especially amongst the men who cannot be passed on to
Teviot Ward, although the most dependent patients are shared
with Bowmont Ward in an endeavour not to overload the staff.
Seven patients are completely helpless and 15 need feeding. Some
also present severe management problems and there was some
anxiety amongst staff at the time of the visit about the management of a male patient who was violently resistive to being
touched.

Philosophy
At a conference organised by Age Concern Scotland in 1984,
Isobel Findlater, the Ettrick Ward charge nurse, described her
objective as being to move, 'albeit slowly and with difficulty',
from 'an ultra traditional approach' in which 'the nurse's role
was toileting, bowel and bladder care, caring for the sick, linen
cupboard, sluices and nothing else' to a situation in which:

'Patients are no longer treated routinely; they are individually
assessed from day to day and their needs met. We never assume,
because a patient cannot participate fully one day, that they
have deteriorated. Skills to a certain extent, if given the
opportunity, can be relearned by the confused person ...
Behavioural problems are now more often as not related to
boredom, and so we established some form of diversion

therapy. Geriatric chairs and sedation are rarely ever considered, never mind used. Personalised clothing, a sense of identity, freedom to choose even if directed, socialising, participation in groups, holidays, bus outings were planned, and with perseverance, carried out successfully, although met with resistance and criticism from both ward staff and outsiders. . . .
It became important to us that the relatives should be part of our group. We set out to involve them, and break down barriers by initially inviting them formally to a coffee afternoon to meet the staff. We encouraged them to feel part of the caring team. We offered support for home visits and outings. We also discuss our plans with them fully at various social occasions. We like to think of ourselves as a family. We respect and comfort each other and argue as necessary.'

However, since this talk was given, the high physical-dependency levels noted above, together with staffing difficulties, have made it increasingly difficult to put these principles fully into practice.

Staffing
Staff levels
At the time of the visit the ward day staff comprised two charge nurses; one staff nurse (there was also a vacant staff nurse post); two SENs; ten wte nursing assistants and three ward orderlies (one part-time). There were also two 'activity assistants'—young people who have come straight from school, usually for a trial before applying for nursing training. They work from 9 am to 5 pm and undertake everything, except strictly nursing duties, including group work, activities, trips, encouragement of self care, and reading or writing with patients. The day staffing level is 21.3 hours per patient week (if the 'activity assistants' and ward orderlies are excluded but charge nurses included), which is by far the lowest of the NHS establishments described in this study. Isobel Findlater estimates that five staff need to be on duty at one time as a bare minimum for safety, and that six is a workable number. Four staff are normally on duty at night, but there were only three on the night of the visit.

Staff qualifications and training
Isobel Findlater and the staff nurse are RMN, the other charge nurse is SRN/RMN, and there are two SENs. All other staff are untrained in professional terms, but the heavy emphasis on staff communication and contribution to decision-making (see below) means that there is a constant input for all grades of staff. In

addition, the hospital runs seminars and in-service courses on a wide range of subjects.

Staff communication

The 'Dingleton approach' puts heavy emphasis on communication at all levels as an inherent part of hospital administration as well as clinical practice. As the psychogeriatrician, Dr Rathie Guldberg, describes it:

> 'authentic consultancy ... depends on everyone consulting everyone else about hospital affairs—for example, personalised laundry, medication, nursing process and group work, and out of these consultations creating thoughts and ideas about the community and the individual's situation, which facilitates growth.'

At the centre of this system is the hospital's community council which meets four times weekly for 50 minutes. This is a multi-disciplinary, decision-making body open to all Dingleton personnel. Patients can attend, but do not often do so. There are no elected representatives at this meeting, but in practice staff from all parts of the hospital and all disciplines attend. There is also a half-hour daily meeting of a management team consisting of three consultants, the director of nursing services, the principal social worker and the sector administrator. The task of this group is mainly to highlight issues which should be taken to the community council and to deal with minor administrative matters. Again, attendance is open to anyone, though usually outsiders come only if they have particular business to discuss. The management team reports upon its deliberations to the community council.

Each specialist team, including the psychogeriatric team, holds regular multi-disciplinary meetings which are attended by as many staff as possible and which also report back to the community council. Dr Guldberg sees the existence of such a team as vital, since it: improves the organisation of resources in the hospital; gives those working with the confused elderly a sense of corporate identity; gives a focus for the efforts of those who want to improve the lot of older patients; and means that there is a more powerful voice speaking for the rights of elderly confused people within the hospital community.

The system of shared responsibility is equally important at ward level. There is a weekly meeting of all staff on Ettrick Ward to discuss ward administration, and a fortnightly 'sensitivity group' which is used for training and for free discussion of frustrations and problems arising from any aspect of work. On alternative fortnights the same time is used for an 'assessment meeting' at which patients who are giving particular concern are discussed and management decisions made relating to their care. Dr Guldberg comes to both these meetings whenever possible, and they are attended by all staff on duty, including ward orderlies, though this concept of 'work' is not given a high priority by the new domestic staff managers.

Regime
Getting up and going to bed
All dressing of patients is done by the daytime staff and no one was up at 7.45 am. Patients are taken to the dining room as soon as they are dressed and, as breakfast is not served until 8.30 am, some of them may have to wait half an hour. Breakfast is available till 10.30 am, however, so there is no need to rush or put pressure on people to wake up; patients are encouraged to have a 'lie in' on their bath morning. Going to bed is also a gradual process which is not started till after 9 pm.

Meals
The dining room, as was noted above, is really part of the huge day room, but separated from the sitting area by the ward office. The general atmosphere is bare, though an attempt has been made to brighten the room with artificial and real pot plants. Patients sit four to a table and these are laid according to ability to use cutlery. When everyone is present, the room is crowded and it is difficult to provide the help required. The staff would like to have two sittings at lunch, but this is not possible because the staff dining room would be closed when the staff needed it. Breakfast consists of cornflakes or porridge, filled rolls and tea. Lunch originally included a soup course, but this has been stopped because it was found to be too much for the patients, so there is now a main course and pudding. A two-course meal is also provided at tea time, but this is too heavy and too close to lunch for elderly patients to cope with. A hot drink and biscuit is provided later on. As a treat supper is occasionally brought in using personal allowances (fish and chips are popular). Staff take account of known tastes of patients when ordering food and need to order a lot of soft food because most patients no longer have teeth. The food is criticised by staff as being too geared to

the tastes of younger patients: 'if you give our patients curry they think the meat has gone off'. Odd snacks and sandwiches can always be provided for individuals from the ward pantry if required. As was noted above, half the patients need assistance with eating.

Activities
Although the 'philosophy' of the ward puts a lot of emphasis on encouraging activities, the high level of dependency and lack of conveniently-placed WCs means that a great deal of time is expended on basic physical care and especially on toiletting. Very little else seemed to be happening on the day of the visit. However, when staffing levels permit, patients are taken in groups of ten to the day centre room and spend the whole day there. The centre is a little distance from the ward and is on a different level, so that there is a sense of change and 'going out'.

The smaller group makes more individual attention possible, and patients are involved in preparing, serving and washing-up the midday meal as well as other activities. They are said to benefit very considerably, but staff shortages and competition with Eddleston Ward for use of the centre restrict its availability. Staff members also take patients into the town on a one-to-one basis, and groups of patients are taken to any appropriate social acitivity in other parts of the hospital. On Saturday evenings alcoholic drinks are served and there is a singsong and perhaps a slide-show of a past holiday or other activity. The annual holiday is *the* event of the year. Staff take patients in groups of five to stay in holiday chalets for a week. As is noted elsewhere in this report, these holidays are a great success in terms of patients' improved response and social skills and greater staff awareness of the potential capacity of individuals. However, it has proved impossible to maintain the higher level of functioning after the return to institutionalised living.

Clothing
All daytime clothing is personal. It is washed in the hospital laundry and stored centrally in the ward. Staff do their best to maintain individuality and quality, but sometimes feel it is a losing battle. New clothes are brought in by relatives or bought from the personal allowance by staff on behalf of patients, or on a visit to the town. A contractor will also provide made-to-measure dresses from a variety of patterns.

Bathing
Baths are normally given weekly during the morning on a rota basis, but the high rate of incontinence means that many patients may require washing several times a day.

Management of continence
By day: Patients are toiletted on a routine basis before and after meals (only one patient is capable of self care). Because of the high level of physical disability and the distance of the WCs from the day room, extensive use is made of wheelchairs to take patients to and from the toilet. Incontinence pads are used if necessary. Maintaining continence appears to dominate the nursing task.

By night: Four staff members are normally on duty at night, though only three were available on the day of the visit; one of these was a charge nurse from the acute admission unit who was standing in for an SEN who was sick. Night staff sit at a desk in the sleeping area and give attention as necessary. Two helpless patients are turned regularly to prevent bed sores. Incontinence pads are used and there is also extensive use of cotsides. Privacy is well-preserved by the use of cubicle curtains.

Reviews
There is no system of individual goal-setting or key worker responsibility for maintaining records, since it is felt that too much concentration on writing-up notes detracts from direct care giving. Patients are reviewed once a fortnight at the assessment meeting, but most time is given to patients about whom staff are feeling particular concern. As was noted above, all members of the ward staff are encouraged to attend and contribute at these meetings.

Personal allowance
This is held by the hospital and used at ward staff discretion to buy clothing, extra food and drink, and to pay for expenses on holidays and outings. Ward staff receive a weekly printout of patients' funds and balances.

Involvement with relatives
Because many relatives felt threatened or bewildered by the move away from traditional nursing practices, uniforms, and rigid routines, time and trouble was needed to help them come to terms with the changes and feel that they had become part of

the caring team. The process was started by formally inviting them to a coffee afternoon to meet the staff, and this was followed up by offering support for home visits and outings and discussing plans with them at other social occasions. However, the psychiatric hospital setting makes it difficult to break down the barriers between relatives and staff and it is sometimes impossible to do so. Also, the shortage of beds and other community support facilities means that often relatives have been driven to breaking point before an admission becomes possible and they then no longer wish to accept responsibility or involvement.

Day care and respite care
Ettrick Ward does not offer these facilities, but Traquair does have some beds which can be booked well in advance to enable supporters to go on holiday, and Glentress sees flexible day care and respite care as part of its role.

Assessment and admission procedures
Patients admitted for assessment to Traquair Ward are carefully monitored over a six-week period and the CAPE rating scale (see page 151) is completed before admission, at intervals during the period of assessment, and at discharge. Hospital staff would greatly prefer to provide assessment as a community-based service, but they see the process as an important means of enabling community support to be tailored to individual need, preventing crisis decision-making and ensuring that physical illness is recognised and treated. All too often, however, despite a decision that longstay care is required, the resources are not available and the patient is discharged inappropriately or remains to 'block' a short-term bed. Few people are admitted to Ettrick Ward as a direct result of the assessment process. Usually they spend some time on another ward and are moved on when they become too dependent, too difficult to manage or need more physical space. (Eddleston Ward, for example, is very cramped.) More commonly, a patient who has been on the waiting list for a long time is admitted direct from the community when an Ettrick bed becomes vacant without going through Traquair. The relevance of the assessment process to Ettrick patients is therefore limited.

Professional support services
General practitioners
GPs come into each psychogeriatic ward on a weekly sessional

basis to look after the physical wellbeing of the patients. They stagger their days of attendance so that a GP is always available.

Consultant psychogeriatrician
Dr Rathie Guldberg has clinical responsibility for the psychogeriatric service provided on the wards and in the community, but she is also responsible for representing psychogeriatrics in the hospital management team and for dealing with *all* new psychiatric referrals within the Ettrick district. There is no way in which she could carry out this task without extensive delegation of responsibility and closely-shared team work, and she would not want to do so. She told a conference held at Dingleton:

> 'One of the most important factors to mention is that the doctor, including the consultant, must be willing to relinquish power and responsibility; as a corollary of this, other members of the team must be willing to accept this power and responsibility. The consultant must be a 'facilitator' in the team helping others to communicate. S/he must exhibit genuine concern, enthusiasm and involvement with 'minor' issues and with 'major' administrative ones, including formulating, with other staff, plans for the long term, and policies and strategies to achieve these.'

In her view, the demand for longstay psychogeriatric beds will not be satisfied within the foreseeable future without the continued use of hospital wards, and the quality of life in these wards must therefore be made as high as possible. 'We must also forge ahead with demands for intermediate or continuing care units nearer the patients' home town' and the need to influence board policy in this direction 'is one of our important tasks'. Within the hospital, she sees her primary role as the provision of clinical and management support to the charge nurses who run the wards, while giving them as free a hand as possible to work with their staff and patients to create their own ethos.

Social services
The community psychiatric nurses and charge nurses, who work as part of the psychogeriatric team but are responsible for community care, hold regular meetings with social services representatives and give much support in local authority homes. Local authority social workers also have access to the three day care units run by the hospital staff. However, the extensive catchment area, the lack of resources and the team's additional

responsibility for providing an acute psychiatric service in the Ettrick district of the Dingleton catchment area, stretches available staff to the limit, so that the service offered is poorer than would be wished. The resulting sense of inadequacy puts a lot of strain on the team's fieldwork staff and this has a knock-on effect on their relationships both in the hospital and the community. Only really effective decentralisation and the multiplication of local resource centres could overcome this problem. Consideration is being given to the conversion of a former nurses' home in Peebles for use as a continuing care unit, and to the possibility of associating facilities with some of the cottage hospitals, whose function will change when the DGH is completed. (There is, however, no wish to share facilities with geriatrics which is seen to be too medical and too rigid in its approach to mix with psychiatry.)

Summary
The psychogeriatric team at Dingleton has made a valiant attempt to put the principles of the therapeutic community into practice on the hosital wards and to offer their patients a decent quality of life. The attempt has not fully succeeded, and there are obvious problems and difficulties in caring for patients in the middle range of dependency presented by Ettrick Ward. Less severely disabled patients on Glentress can be offered a regime in which concepts of rehabilitation and discharge have some meaning, while the very helpless patients in Teviot Ward are receiving a high quality of tender loving care which probably could not be provided much better elsewhere. On Ettrick Ward, however, the utterly unsuitable physical surroundings, the immense pressure of both physical and mental dependency and the institutional restrictions of hospital life dominate the day's routine, whatever staff aspirations may be. All that can be done is to alleviate their worst effects. The staff on this ward and the psychogeriatric team in general are unanimous in wanting to provide more care in small, localised units and reduce the number of beds in the base psychiatric hospital. The 14 years' experiment in psychogeriatric care can, therefore, be said not to have been wholly successful, but if it has generated enough pressure to make community-based units a reality, it will in fact have succeeded.

Non-statutory provision
Private sector

HIGHLAND HOUSE
28 Austin Street, Hunstanton, Nr Kings Lynn, Norfolk: Tel–Hunstanton 34180
Proprietor—Mrs Joyce Bergin

Principal characteristics

Highland House is a private ten-bedded residential home which operates on a very domestic pattern, the proprietor and her family being closely involved in care provision. It represents one end of the scale of 'specialised care' described in this report, and the severity and nature of disability catered for at any one time varies considerably. Its main interest lies in the approach of a proprietor whose professional training was in occupational therapy to the management of people with dementia and behavioural disorders in a 'guest house' type setting.

History

The proprietor had considerable experience as a hospital-based OT working with severely disabled people. She had long aspired to run her own residential home and 'trained herself' to do so by undertaking clerical work, in which she learned book-keeping, accounts and record-keeping, and then by working as an auxiliary nurse in a private nursing home. Capital to buy Highland House, and the proprietor's own house which adjoins it, was obtained by selling her original home, her husband working in the Middle East for eighteen months and the use of savings. All present profits are ploughed back into improvements. The home started in 1982 with one resident and has built up its full complement gradually. The original intention had not been to operate as a specialist home, but the proprietor acquired a reputation for dealing with people with mental disability and she gradually accumulated this kind of client—starting with those who were 'nicely muddled' and building to more severely disabled people when she found that she could cope.

Design and furnishing

Highland House is a three-storey Edwardian terraced house in a small country town and seaside resort on the North Norfolk coast. Apart from an inconspicuous board saying 'home for the elderly' there is nothing to indicate that it is not a private residence. It connects at ground floor and top floor level with the proprietor's house next door. (Various alterations have been made since the visit to create better use of space.)

It provides three double and four single bedrooms, one of which is on the ground floor (this was formerly a reception room). Bedrooms are exceptionally well furnished to a good 'hotel' standard, but washbasins in shared rooms are not screened. Residents can bring in their own furniture (but at the time of the original visit few had done so) and much encouragement has to be given to persuade relatives to bring in photographs and small items. The lounge is carpeted and well supplied with ornaments, pictures, coffee tables, and so on, and most of the chairs are of a wing-type and covered in tapestry. A very small dining room has been built on to the kitchen. The atmosphere on the ground floor is domestic, but it is also cramped. There is a bathroom with en-suite lavatory on each of the upper floors and a small WC on the ground floor which is very awkwardly placed just inside the front door. The stairs are narrow and steep, though a stair-lift which goes most of the way to the first floor has now been fitted. In general, the building illustrates very clearly all the advantages and disadvantages of using converted premises for this purpose. It is friendly, domestic and familiar, but the very cramped ground floor and difficulty of access to bedrooms generate considerable problems which are exacerbated when residents who are severely physically or mentally disabled are being cared for.

Ability range of residents
At the time of the initial visit the average score on the CRBRS was 4.2 with only three residents rating 7–10 and five 0–3. However, this score does not reflect overall disability. One lucid resident is 95 and totally deaf so that communication with her demands considerable skill, and the other lucid resident is subject to acute confusional states and histrionic 'bad turns'. Three others show severe, though intermittent, behavioural disturbance. On the other hand, the resident rated 10, who was chairbound at the time of the initial visit, had improved so much some weeks later (largely as a result of having been taken off the sedative drugs she was taking before admission) that she was mobile with assistance and able to communicate at a simple level. Her score

had thus dropped to about 7. However, a new mentally-alert resident who had suffered a stroke had been added to the 7–10 group. This was a very heavy, chairfast man who could only be lifted with the help of the proprietor's husband. He had been living in isolation at home and was said to enjoy the company, limited as it was, as well as the care. In physical terms he added greatly to the level of a dependency carried by the home, but brought the CRBRS score down still further. On a third follow-up visit some months later this gentleman had died and the home had taken in three successive patients from Hellesden psychiatric hospital all of whom had died within six to ten weeks. This experience caused considerable distress and the proprietor's response was to let a double room to a mentally-alert though socially isolated couple who had previously been living in sheltered housing and were finding it difficult to cope. They have furnished the room themselves and eat their meals there so that there is little contact with anyone except the proprietor. Again this change will bring the overall level of mental disability down and it is an indication of the need to take care when making referrals to a small home of this kind, to ensure that the staff do not get discouraged and look for a less demanding and less distressing task.

Philosophy
This stems from the proprietor's attitude rather than from theory. She selects gentle, soft-spoken staff whose personalities she likes, and encourages them, by her own example, to use trust, established relationships and persuasion to obtain co-operation. 'There are no hard and fast rules and no chivvying'. The stated emphasis is on awareness of what residents can manage from day to day and what level of care they need rather than trying to stick to established regimes however 'individualised' they may be. 'Abilities change within twenty-four hours.'

At the time of the visit the front door was always kept locked with the key removed, but it is now open in the daytime. There is free access into the back garden and residents are encouraged to share in household activity and to move freely throughout the house.

Staffing
Staff levels
Fourteen part-time staff are employed on five shifts—8 am to 11 am; 11 am to 3 pm; 3 pm to 6 pm; 6 pm to 10 pm and 10 pm

to 8 am. The short shifts make it easier to get staff and the proprietor believes that they are conducive to generating the mental energy needed to cope in a patient and understanding way. Two people are on duty during the daytime and one in the evening and at night. In addition, Mrs Bergin is always about from 8 am to 11 am, and is on call to help out when needed at other times, and members of her family may also give informal help. The daytime staff ratio is thus 16 hours per resident per week, but if the proprietor's time is added this rises to nearly 19.

Staff qualifications and training
The proprietor's own formal and informal training has already been referred to. Apart from one Youth Opportunity trainee, she selects middle-aged female staff whose children have grown up and who have gentle, quiet personalities. It is important that they should be able to be flexible in their shifts to cover holidays and illness. Training is by experience and personal example. 'I have gradually built up staff I can trust.'

Staff communication
This is mainly at a very personal informal level, though an occurrence book is kept to maintain continuity of care between shifts. Most staff wear a simple uniform and address the proprietor formally, either by surname or as 'matron'. The general atmosphere is, however, friendly and informal.

Regime
Getting up and going to bed
The night staff member gives help with toiletting from about 6.30 am when she hears residents begin to move about. They then go back to bed or sit up in dressing gowns and are given breakfast. Most can manage this by themselves or with a little encouragement. Help is given with dressing in a leisurely way as required by day staff after 8 am with emphasis on meeting individual needs and being aware of changing needs. Residents can stay in bed for as long as they wish and on the first visit some were not up by 11 am. 'Everyone is feeling sleepy this morning.' Bedtime is also flexible, but tends to be in two groups. Some like to go at around 7.30 pm and others may stay up till midnight, watching TV with the staff member on duty and often with the proprietor and her family also present.

Meals
As was noted above, breakfast is given on trays in bed around

7 am. Mid-morning coffee in the lounge is followed by lunch at 1 pm in the very small dining room. At the time of the visit, residents sat at tables of four, four and two, according to ability and speed of eating. There was no room for dishes on the tables, but meals were served from the adjoining kitchen, according to taste and request, and the tables were properly laid. (Two sittings have now been arranged.) Personal assistance is given as required, usually when the faster eaters have left. Care staff do all the cooking and washing-up, but ready-cooked pies, trifles and so on, may be bought if necessary. A snack of fresh fruit and tea is served in the lounge at about 3.15 pm. The last main meal is at 5.30 pm with sherry as a regular 'night cap' around 7 pm, and a late night drink is available for those who are still up. The impression is that the small size of the group, the accessibility of the kitchen, and the absence of any specialist kitchen staff encourages maximum flexibility and resident involvement.

Activities

Apart from a weekly visit from the hairdresser (who attends to all the women residents) there were no formal activities at the time of the first visit, except for a discussion of the daily paper and general chat in the lounge where almost constant TV discourages communication. (Minibus outings and a weekly singsong/recall session with a visiting entertainer are now taking place.) Residents are encouraged to help with washing up and carrying crockery, and have free access to the kitchen. Some can read papers and books and a librarian calls regularly. The main form of activity, however, is going out into the town. A group of residents regularly attend a local church where eccentricity of behaviour is accepted and where the congregation will help with transport if needed. There are visits to shows at the local theatre and individual shopping trips to the Kings Lynn market or local shops. Reaction to a restless resident, Mrs Bergin said, would be 'to take her for a walk and have a cup of coffee outside'. One resident had tried going to a local day centre, but she had been reluctant to continue. 'I can have a cup of coffee at home just as well.' The position of Highland House near the centre of the town, and the familiarity of the surroundings help to maintain normal patterns of this kind.

Clothing

Clothes are bought in consultation with residents and are well looked after by staff. They clearly reflect previous role and personality. One resident, for example, who was formerly a buyer for Harrods, has a positively regal appearance.

Bathing

Bathing is normally provided to the same routine for each individual, though this may vary from one to three baths a week. Extra ones are fitted in if they are asked for or needed. All bathing is supervised in the sense of getting it ready, helping the person in, scrubbing the back and offering other help, but the person is left alone to wash and soak if they prefer this. The emphasis is on providing as normal a procedure as possible rather than using bath seats and gadgets, and the proprietor says that her OT training has 'given her the knack' of getting very disabled people in and out single-handed. Originally she did all the bathing herself, but has now trained an assistant to her satisfaction.

Management of continence

By day: People with incontinence problems are taken to the toilet twenty minutes after drinks have been served and incontinence pads are used as required. Residents are followed to the WC and cleaned up quietly if necessary. Public comment is avoided, but several chairs in the lounge have Inco sheets on them. There is no smell, a fact which Mrs Bergin attributes to immediate clearing up after an accident and a very conscientious cleaner.

By night: All bedroom doors are left open and residents are checked regularly by looking through them. If movement is heard at any time, assistance is given as necessary. All rooms have commodes, and beds are fitted with waterproof sheets. A catheter may be used in the case of heavy incontinence in a dying resident.

Reviews

No review system is felt to be necessary because of close personal knowledge of residents.

Personal allowance

No resident had the custody of their own allowance at the time of the initial visit, though some were mentally able to manage this.

Involvement with relatives

The proprietor is on first-name terms with relatives, who are mainly local people, and they have free access at any time and are encouraged to take residents out. Two families were visited to ask their opinion of the home. One son and daughter-in-law of the very disabled lady (CRBRS score 10) who is now improving, said that the care, personal knowledge and attention experienced at Highland House was in strong contrast to a previous home where she had been very distressed. The second family (the brother and sister-in-law of a widow suffering from an early dementia complicated by narcolepsy) were pleased with a close relationship which she had formed with another resident with whom she shared a room and felt the care was good, though they did not have experience of another home with which to compare it. They were slightly concerned at the lack of regular occupation and thought that the home had become a bit crowded. They felt that eight residents would be preferable in the accommodation available. However, they emphasised that the resident is happy there and sees it as her home. Her son would have taken her to live with him in Australia, but she did not want to go.

Volunteers
Volunteers are not used in the home, apart from the informal support of Mrs Bergin's family and the families of other staff.

Respite care
Empty beds are used for holiday or emergency care on an *ad hoc* basis.

Assessment and admission and discharge procedures
Referral may be from the GP, social worker or psychiatric hospital. As was noted above, hospital referrals have recently proved disastrous and Mrs Bergin takes those from the social worker 'with a pinch of salt' since they tend to understate the level of disability involved; GP referral is therefore preferred. There is no formal admission procedure and the prospective resident usually accepts the GP's recommendation for a trial stay without even asking for a preliminary visit. The proprietor does, however, often visit the person at home and offers to transport her herself. She always emphasises to relatives that no action should be taken to dispose of property until it is clear that the placement is going to be successful—which she says becomes apparent within a month. Residents are not discharged for any physical illness or any level of incontinence, and several residents have been cared for till death, which is usually preceded by a fairly short period of 'fading' rather than a long illness. Mrs Bergin has, however, refused to keep a longstay resident who was too well mentally and, as a result, was able to dominate and bully other residents. Several very difficult people have been

coped with from time to time, though not simultaneously. It is not clear to what degree the generally well-socialised behaviour of the present residents is a result of Mrs Bergin's management skills and the familiar domestic setting, or a reflection of referral and admission policy, but the nature of the house and the current level of staffing would seem to preclude coping with a group of very disturbed people.

Professional support services
Psychiatric services
There is no specialist psychogeriatric service of any kind in the area. The one acute psychiatric ward at Queen Elizabeth Hospital, Kings Lynn, would not accept any patients with organic illness. The nearest psychiatric hospital is Hellesdon near Norwich, which is over 40 miles away, and it is said to be quite impossible to get female patients admitted for long term-care but it is slightly easier for men. 'The private sector take the lot' according to the GP, and it is noteworthy that this is done without any specialist psychiatric or CPN backing. (The area also has no longstay geriatric beds available for admissions from the community. Those which do exist are exclusively used to 'unblock' beds in the acute wards.)

Social work services
There is a social work sub-district office based in Hunstanton, but it is rather out on a limb—the main district office being sited in Fakenham and most of the available resources in another SSD district based in Kings Lynn. There are five social workers in the Hunstanton office of whom three are trained. One of the untrained assistants specialises in work with elderly people, though the others 'do their share'. One Part III home is about to be closed because it is physically unsuitable, and it is intended that the resources made available will be used for the provision of sheltered housing (in partnership with a housing association), day care and more intensive home help, but these services are not yet available. The Hunstanton office has access to half the beds in another Part III home, but the OIC can also admit independently and can refuse to accept an SSD referral if the proposed resident is likely to 'upset the balance of dependency in the home'. Obtaining an SSD place for a client with dementia is very difficult. Social services is therefore very heavily reliant on the private sector, and the development of private residential care has filled a major gap.

General practitioner

All Highland House residents are registered with one general practice which shares premises with the district nursing service. The senior partner is felt by Mrs Bergin to have been most helpful in referring suitable residents and in supporting her as she built up experience in managing mental disability as well as in providing medical treatment for her residents. However, the partner who was interviewed was most emphatic concerning the problems which the concentration of private homes in the area was causing the practice. At one time, he said, they had five homes in the area and used to visit regularly on a fortnightly basis. Now they have eighteen and 'are back to crisis medicine'. Additional problems are caused by the fact that the only new houses to be built in the area are two-bedroom bungalows, which are often taken up by retired people in poor health. Nearly 40 per cent of patients in the practice are over 65 and many have come from as far as Nottingham and Leicester. 'There is no way in which the local population could supply the market.' The large number of private homes and nursing homes and the DHSS payment of fees does, however, mean that the practice now has few patients living in squalor and danger since 'we can get a bed for anyone who needs it'. This doctor does not think that the Highland House residents are unusual in their level of mental disturbance, they 'are just concentrated in a smaller number'. He says many residential homes keep residents who become demented 'because there is no alternative' and the standard of care is generally good. However, if he had a patient with severe dementia who required admission he would try to find a nursing home place.

District nursing service

It was not possible to meet a district nurse, but it is clear that they provide a very supportive service to the residential homes in the area and Mrs Bergin had nothing but praise for their help. However, in the GP's opinion, the service is also being overloaded by the concentration of homes in the area and by the consequent heavy demand for incontinence pads and ripple beds: he believes they could not cope if many homes did not, in fact, use their own staff to do what are technically nursing tasks.

Summary

Highland House is an example of the very small specialist provision in the private sector which can be expected to develop in the face of fierce competition for residents and the high demand in areas which still have very poor psychogeriatric provision and a large population of elderly people. The skill and dedication of this particular proprietor and her real interest in this area of work have resulted in a high quality of care in this instance, in spite of the cramped nature of the ground floor accommodation and the inaccessibility of bedrooms. It is, however, clear that a specialist home of this kind is very vulnerable. In the first place, it depends on the continued good health of the proprietor. She has just got to the point where she feels she can risk taking a short holiday, but any prolonged absence would create major problems for both residents and staff. This is, of course, the case with many small, private homes, but the mental disabilities of the residents and the need for skilled management would make any temporary replacement much more problematic. Second, any continued very disturbed behaviour would be exceedingly difficult to cope with in the absence of a psychogeriatric back-up service to advise on management and, if necessary, to arrange a hospital admittance. Third, homes like this provide a valuable resource for moderately disabled residents, but if hospital social workers or other professionals refer residents who are not suitable, the staff will either become grossly over-burdened or turn to a less demanding field of care. Mrs Bergin's decision to admit a relatively independent couple in place of the frail and demented people referred from Hellesdon Hospital is an excellent example of the need for great care in making placements in a home of this kind.

KILNCROFT
27/29 Ashburnham Road, Hastings TN35 3JN:
Tel–Hastings 429737:
Proprietor: Mr Richard Padgett

Principal characteristics
Kilncroft is a 27-bedded private residential home in converted premises providing specialist care. It is owned and run by a nurse with SRN/RMN training and with extensive charge nurse experience and it has become the pilot scheme for a further small group of specialist homes with centralised financial management and staff supervision. This group is run as a limited company called Croft. It currently has two homes in Tunbridge Wells and Bromley, and a further, purpose-built, one is being planned. Kilncroft is thus of interest in terms of the way in which it is managed and run, the quality of care offered, its relationship with statutory services, and its position as the pioneer of a 'chain' of specialist homes.

History
Following his extensive experience in the psychogeriatric field, the proprietor, Richard Padgett, came to believe that he could run a home which offered better care than is usually provided in the NHS. In 1980 he and his wife started with a three-storey semi-detached Victorian house on the outskirts of Hastings, and built up from a small group of three residents to a registered home for ten residents. The neighbouring house then became vacant and was added to the home providing another 17 beds. During this process Richard Padgett acquired necessary expertise on the accountancy and management side of the business and used this to establish Croft Residential Homes in which he is a partner. Kilncroft is, however, still financially independent of Croft, though the three homes are run in close association and Kilncroft is used as a source of expertise and a base for staff training and management.

Design and furnishing
The two adjoining houses each have a front room used as a lounge, one for about ten of the more alert residents and the other for the remainder. Two other ground floor rooms in each

house are used as double bedrooms. A large dining/activities room has been built on to the backs of both houses plus a kitchen and small office. It is only possible to go from one house to the other on the ground floor by passing through the dining room. The first and second floors provide four more double rooms, five singles and two three-bedded rooms, together with one Parker bath and WC, two other bathrooms and five other WCs. There is also a WC off each ground floor passage close to the dining room. These are small and awkward, but because of their position, they are in by far the heaviest use. A stair lift and sluice are planned.

Furnishing and decoration is domestic in type and scale, and the bedrooms have a pleasing lack of uniformity in shape and furniture and furnishings with plentiful personal ornaments and pictures. It has, however, become necessary to take up more and more carpets as residents become incontinent. There is no provision for personal privacy within the shared rooms and one of the most pleasant bedrooms, used by three of the most alert residents, is also used by staff to interview visitors, since there is no suitable space for this. No bedroom doors are knocked on when showing visitors round. Access to the bedrooms is free for all residents and several of the more alert and physically able make considerable use of this. One resident also likes to spend much of her time sitting on the stairs. Occasional falls have occurred as a result of free access to the upper floors, but this is not thought to be a sufficient reason to restrict movement. The front door is kept locked and, at the time of the visit, the key was in the charge of a staff member, but this system has now been replaced with a digital lock in order to eliminate 'the institutional key'. There is access, via the kitchen, to a patio at the back and the street can also be reached by this means.

Ability range of residents
As with the other non-statutory homes included in this study, the ability range is wide. Four residents scored 0–3 on the CRBRS scale and nine scored 10 or 11, so the overall average of 7.5 is rather misleading. Of the six more able residents (0–5), one was in the original group of three admitted before the concept of specialisation was worked out. She suffers from anxiety and agitation, is not capable of independent living, and has become very dependent on the home and proprietor. She enjoys feeling superior to the other residents and sees herself as a 'helper'. She can go out freely via the back door. The second suffers from

severe though intermittent depression which mimics dementia, and the third is nearly blind and was admitted in a toxic confusional state which turned out to be temporary, but is very happy in the home. The fourth is the severely-arthritic father of the senior member of the care staff and having him as a resident enables her to continue with her job. He isolates himself for most of the day by sitting and smoking in the dining room close to the kitchen door. The remaining two are suffering respectively from brain damage caused by a stroke and from an early dementia. One resident was chair-bound and clearly very unwell at the time of the visit. She also spent the day in the dining room where staff could most easily observe her. Most of the remaining residents were fairly active compared with other homes observed in this study, and were capable of a considerable amount of self care and self feeding. Padgett attributes this to the policy of encouraging mobility and using minimal sedation.

Philosophy
A statement of 'the Croft concept of care' intended for prospective staff members says:

'The greatest principles are usually the simplest. Human beings, whatever their situation, generally thrive in an interesting, home-like environment. This is what we at Croft believe in. Dementia may take its toll of memory, thinking and reasoning, control over ordinary functions, and so on, but within every victim of the disease resides the need to be *involved* and to be *comfortable*.

We believe that people—people who may be our mothers, our fathers, eventually ourselves—should not become inert and institutionalized. Such a state of affairs is not only heartless and thoughtless, it is clinically detrimental in that it accelerates the decline of the individual.

So, the principle of care is that each resident for whom we care is the person for whom we care most. We shall have our good days and our not so good days, but the principle remains the same.

This principle of care breaks down if the *carers* do not feel involved and comfortable. Working with the elderly confused and psychologically frail is exceptionally demanding: 'many are called but few are chosen'. We expect to lose a proportion of recruits in their early days. It is important to be open and frank in appropriate ways and settings when tensions or uncertainties arise. We encourage all members of staff to speak out their worries, gripes, suggestions and questions to the person who is next in line. In demanding occupations, molehills quickly become mountains.'

Richard Padgett believes that a well-established routine, skilled management and plenty of activities will maintain dementia sufferers on a 'plateau' and prevent further deterioration in functioning, provided they are not already severely disabled. He is, therefore, in a constant dilemma between admitting severely disabled people who are in most acute need of care, and admitting those whom he feels he can help most, though those who could be easily managed elsewhere would not be accepted. Kilncroft will look after residents with short-term or terminal illness (usually moving them to a ground floor room), but is not geared to cope with those who are likely to be immobile over a long period, and would not keep residents whose dementia is so severe that they are unaware of their environment and unable to profit from it. It is felt that this would not be a proper use of the facilities. In spite of the small group of functionally-ill residents, the home is intended to cater for people with some form of dementia, and avoids mixing different types of illness as far as possible.

So far, two people have proved unmanageable in this setting. One was an active man of 57 with early dementia who was wandering and aggressive and showed no response to tranquillisers, and the other a woman with no dementia but a florid personality and behaviour disorder who was deliberately and promiscuously faecally incontinent.

Staffing
Staff levels
As with the other private homes discussed in this study, extensive use is made of part-time staff. Overall, however, the system provides for four or five people to be on duty from 8 am to 5 pm with two or three in the evening. This gives a day staff ratio per resident week of 17.2 hours. A cook, a part-time domestic and a part-time secretary are also employed. When a senior staff member is not on duty in the home, one is always available at fairly short notice through a radio paging system. At the time of the visit only one member of staff was on duty at night, though another was lodging in a flat attached to the premises. This has now been increased to two waking night staff.

Staff qualifications and training

Apart from the proprietor, only one member of staff has a professional qualification and she is an SEN. The 'executive carer' who has overall responsibility for the quality of care both in Kilncroft and in the Croft homes, is the sister-in-law of the proprietor and was trained by him at Kilncroft. She is hoping to do the CSS course. Staff are normally recruited through the local press and 'trained on-the-job' although there is no checklist of procedures covered and no formal supervision sessions. It is hoped eventually to introduce a key worker system and instruction by a qualified OT on running the activities sessions. In addition to on-the-job training, staff are encouraged to attend the course of care staff run by the local Association of Registered Rest Homes.

All new care staff are provided with a package of information. This includes a job description, which covers: physical care; domestic duties (housekeeping, cooking, laundry, bed-making, care of residents' clothing and food preparation); psychological care ('talking to residents, discussing problems'); and participation in 'orientation and activities'. Flexibility in hours and availability for overtime are written in. The package also contains a copy of the 'Croft concept of care' quoted above, a statement on admission procedures, which will be further discussed below, and a very detailed three-page schedule of the 'daily routine'. The latter is reinforced by a note on the staff noticeboard in the dining/activities room which states:

'While we are very much against running the home on military lines, few things distress you, your residents and their relatives more than a sense of neglect or chaos. To help you achieve an atmosphere of comfortable order, here is a check-list for carers:

Laundry collected and returned; medication set up at proper times; toileting chart in day book; all significant events in day book; domestic work satisfactorily undertaken. At weekends: carry out the tasks described; from time to time count the residents; check that residents have their bath as listed in the bath book.'

(In spite of the disclaimer, this notice is strongly reminiscent of military 'standing orders'.)

Much care is taken about the process of setting up new homes.

The proposed senior carer of each new home works at Kilncroft for a probationary month before the appointment is confirmed, and all the staff then have a week's induction training before residents are admitted. The executive carer and Richard Padgett spend a lot of time during the first three months or so in each new home until they are satisfied that 'the Croft concept of care' is firmly established, and the executive carer makes unscheduled visits to Kilncroft and the Croft homes at all hours of the day and night. She also spends one day a week in each home. In emergency she can be contacted by radio pager.

Staff communication
A 'day book' is maintained in which all incidents of any importance are recorded, including interactions between residents, eating or failing to eat, information about proposed activities and outings with relatives. The senior carer and the proprietor, sometimes with a care assistant, go through the Kardex once a week and discuss symptoms, medication and management in the ensuing week and a weekly individual record is maintained. There is a staff meeting every two months, but this is mainly concerned with wider administrative matters.

Regime
Getting up and going to bed
Residents who are wet at 5 am are got up, rather than risk having to change the bed again at 6 am. Others are got up when the first day staff come on at 6 am. Everyone was dressed on the day of the visit by 7.15 am and tea was being served, but breakfast was not available until 8.30 am. Beds are made while residents are sitting on their commodes or the WC during the getting-up process. A 'long lie' is not allowed except in case of illness, since it is felt that an accustomed routine is beneficial. At night, hot drinks are served at 8.30 pm and dependent residents are then taken to bed in groups according to the floor they are sleeping on. This is because taking people upstairs one by one is such a time-consuming process. Those able to look after themselves are allowed to do so, but there is a strong expectation that everyone will be in bed when the evening staff go off at 10 pm. The system is not rigid, however. For example, the resident who prefers to spend most of her time sitting on the stairs also refused to go to bed on the night of the visit and was eventually persuaded to lie down on the settee in the lounge.

Meals
As was explained above, a good-sized dining room which doubles

as an activity room has been built onto the back of both houses. Square or oblong tables seating four residents each are laid with glass and cutlery and checked tablecloths. The walls are decorated with pictures of animals, photos of past social events, and photographs of residents before they became ill, each with a brief potted biography giving marital status, children and previous occupation. Notices relating to activities are displayed and one corner is used for staff notices, the day book and other records. Breakfast, served at 8.30 am, consists of cornflakes, marmalade, sandwiches and tea. Lunch at 12 noon is a two-course meal cooked on the premises and served plated with second helpings being offered from the serving dish. Tea at 5 pm is a hot snack with bread and butter and tea. Coffee mid-morning, a cup of tea with a biscuit in mid-afternoon during the activities session and a hot drink in the evening are also served. Almost all residents can eat without help and most finish their lunch within half an hour, but care assistants were observed piling up chairs and sweeping the floor around four residents who were slower.

Activities
The daily schedule issued to all staff (see above) states that the morning 'orientation' sessions and afternoon 'activities' (2–4 pm) are 'the most important part of the day'. The 'orientation session' is a discussion about newspaper items with the more able residents in the 'alert' lounge, the paper being collected by a member of the care staff usually accompanied by two residents. On the day of the visit a very lively music and movement session took place with much dancing and clapping and energetic participation by both staff and residents, though people could opt out if they wished to. It was noisy, especially when a resident performed on an electric organ and xylophone, and not very restful for the disabled chairbound resident who was being cared for in the dining room throughout the day. (Kilncroft is now developing a nursing home wing.)

The noticeboard about afternoon activities refers to dominoes, music and movement, quiz games, collage making, board games, knitting, walks, crosswords, crochet, painting, jig-saw puzzles and making pom-poms. In view of the severe disability of some residents, however, the general impression is that the staff have a constant struggle to keep the quality and level of involvement in activities up to the desired level. Padgett would like to appoint an OT who would have a training and supervisory role in all the Croft homes and it is hoped to do this as soon as funds permit. Staff interaction with residents in the lounges is minimal apart from the 'orientation' session, since the layout of the building does not encourage staff entry into the lounges, except for specific purposes, and there is little space for activity. The TV is on fairly constantly with those in the 'less alert' lounge paying no attention to it. Some of the more alert residents are able to read and knit. The senior carer said that the emphasis was on encouraging interaction if someone seemed distressed or wanting attention rather than making contact with residents for its own sake.

A number of organised outings to picnic spots for all staff and residents take place during the summer months, using hired transport, and staff may take residents out for a ride in their own cars, as one did on the day of the visit, or take a small group to the pub in the evening, again using their own car.

Clothing
All clothing is personal and kept in residents' own wardrobes. Making sure that clothes are clearly marked is part of the admission procedure, and washing and looking after clothes is part of the care assistant's role. New clothes are normally bought by relatives or by staff on behalf of residents using their personal allowance. Sales representatives are encouraged. All residents were appropriately dressed.

Bathing
Baths are given weekly between 6 and 7 pm according to a set schedule unless they are required more often.

Management of continence
By day: A new toileting chart is made out each day in the day book for all incontinent residents and checked off for everyone on a strictly maintained two-hour toileting schedule, and the senior carer described the 'sense of triumph' felt by staff who had managed to keep an incontinent patient dry all day. Kanga pants are used if required for physically disabled people, but there are no incontinence sheets on chairs. Catheterisation would be considered if other methods had failed, but this is avoided if possible because of the likelihood that the catheter would be pulled out and the danger of infection. Constipation is kept at a minimum with orange juice, high fibre food etc, and by a constant check on bowel movement in the toileting chart. If necessary the proprietor or staff trained by him give regular or occasional enemas.

By night: The two-hourly toiletting routine is continued through-out the night for those who are felt to need it. Staff members are said to feel that 'it sometimes is a shame to wake them', but the proprietor is convinced that it is worth the disturbance in terms of quality of life and freedom from skin troubles. He encourages the use of lavatories rather than commodes, but these are necessary in a number of cases.

Reviews
The only routine review is the weekly check through the Kardex by the proprietor and senior carer. Residents who are giving cause for concern are discussed on an informal basis as often as necessary.

Personal allowance
Almost all residents were receiving the constant attendance allowance and this is used to make up their fees. About half the residents had the bulk of their fees paid through social security with any shortfall being made up by relatives (at the time of the visit the home had just been re-registered as catering for 'mental handicap' so a higher supplementary benefit rate could be claimed). Personal allowances are credited to the resident and used on their behalf for personal purchases, visits to the pub, chiropody and hairdressing. No residents handle money them-selves because they could not take responsibility for it and the admission procedure discourages any valuables, apart from wedding rings, from being brought in.

Involvement with relatives
The proprietor sees it as part of his role to 'counsel' relatives, and to provide the information about the dementing illness and its prognosis which should have been given by the GP but often has not been. Some visitors often drop in for a chat with the staff and other residents as well as their 'own' relative and seem to enjoy coming, but there is considerable personal variation in this regard, and there is no formal system of relatives' support. One daughter of a resident, a professional social worker, said she had been impressed by the way in which her mother had settled when other environments, including day care in a hospital ward, had proved unsatisfactory. She supported the use of shared rooms for people with dementia on the ground that her mother is less apt to think it is time to get up if she wakes up and knows that someone else is in the room and asleep. She also supported the steady routine as necessary for dementia sufferers and spoke

highly of the motivation of staff and the quality of physical care offered.

Volunteers
Volunteers are not involved in the home, apart from participation of the families of the proprietor and staff and relatives of residents in organising parties and outings.

Assessment and admission procedures
Referrals come from hospital-based staff, social services, a private social worker and GPs. The proprietor does his own assessment, using a form he designed himself, which includes: the usual personal and financial details; a 'mental score questionnaire' of ten basic questions; a detailed series of headings relating to habits and abilities, mental and physical; a brief life history; involvement and visiting patterns of relatives and friends; and a summary under the headings: diagnosis (apparent or confirmed); onset (of dementia/personality change); stage (early/moderate/advanced); suitability for Croft home; and special observations. This form is completed on the basis of his own observation and information from the referrer, doctor and relatives. He sometimes makes a home visit but this is not routine, since the prospective resident may be seen in hospital or another home, or on a preliminary visit to Kilncroft. A brochure is available giving basic information about the home, and care is taken to talk to the responsible relative about the 'Croft concept of care', the need to accept some degree of risk, and the possibility that there will be an initial period of deterioration or unhappiness while the resident becomes accustomed to the change in environment. He strongly believes (and tries to convince supporters), that a home like Kilncroft can often do more to maintain dementia sufferers at a maximum level of functioning than a relative who is struggling to cope unaided at home. The information pack given to new care staff includes a statement on admission procedures in which the preamble says:

'First impressions are lasting. In the case of the elderly confused, they are crucial. The way in which you receive the new resident and his/her relatives or social worker, is probably the most important procedure you will ever carry out. We all tend to dislike change, especially moving house. Your new resident is likely to be very lost, agitated, doubly confused, sad and possibly quite hostile.

Your manner should be unhurried, calm, welcoming and

confident. Give your whole attention to the resident and whoever is with him or her. Take them to a private place, ideally the resident's room if no one else is in at the time. Arrange for a cup of tea to be brought in, and seat people comfortably. When the resident is settled, tell him/her your name clearly and in simple terms explain your role and the very basic set up in the house. Sometimes the resident will be more responsive to gentle touching than a stream of what might seem confusing talk: if it seems right, hold his or her hand or put your arm around his/her shoulder. Answer any questions or worries either the resident or those with him or her may have.

Bring the resident's belongings into the room and—involving him/her as far as possible—arrange clothing and personal ornaments, photographs where he/she can easily see them. The room door and wardrobe should have been *clearly labelled* beforehand.

Later, show the resident, if he/she is ready and able, the key areas of the house, ie the nearest toilet, the lounge and the dining room.'

The statement goes on to give instructions about various administrative matters, the marking and labelling of clothing and personal possessions (including the resident with a wristband ('just in case he/she gets lost in the the early days') and notifying the kitchen of dietary needs and tastes.

Professional support services
General practitioners
Kilncroft makes little use of any professional support services except for the GP. Residents can keep their own GP if he is within reach, otherwise everyone is registered with one practice where the doctor is friendly and supportive, but not willing to set up a system of routine visiting, and places a lot of trust in the proprietor's nursing knowledge and skills to signal when a change of medication may be needed or health problems have been observed. Staff training puts a lot of emphasis on observing the effect of drugs and obtaining the GP's permission to reduce dosage if sedatives or tranquillisers are appearing to cause drowsiness, since Padgett believes that use of sedatives to this point is a major cause of physical deterioration. (The GP who looks after most of the residents was ill at the time of the visit and could not be interviewed.)

Psychogeriatric services
Hastings is a small town which so far has maintained an atmosphere of personal knowledge and contact between the various branches of the NHS and particularly between the geriatrician, Dr Irvine, who is famous as a pioneer in this field, and the psychogeriatrician, Dr Venkateswarlu (known locally as Dr Venkat) who is also an enthusiastic and able innovator. A DGH is planned to open 1991 (an event not looked forward to with enthusiasm by either doctor). At present St Helen's Hospital, which is a former workhouse, provides medical, paediatric and rehabilitative beds for all categories of patients, while the Royal East Sussex provides surgery, outpatient consultation, and obstetrics and gynaecology. The psychogeriatrician has an eight-bedded assessment ward in St Helens which is used for both disturbed geriatric patients and psychiatric patients who need a lot of medical attention. The two consultants do a combined ward round once a week, and the geriatric houseman checks the patients from the physical point of view.

Dr Venkateswarlu himself now operates from St Anne's House—first-class converted premises, these have been made into a Department of Mental Health for the Elderly (DMHE). Here he has one of the best equipped and most attractive day hospitals seen in the course of this study, as well as a full-time psychologist, a social worker and a team of eight specialist CPNs with their own properly equipped office and secretarial support. With this base he is able to provide community support at a level which leaves empty beds available at Hellingly, the traditional psychiatric hospital which is 20 miles away and is being run down. One ward of 25 beds was due to be closed in the spring of 1986 and the money will be used to set up a specialist home and day centre in co-operation with social services. This is a pioneer project which will be staffed and run jointly by both services and will have two CPNs based in it. It will provide: 34 residential places (some of which will be used for shortstay and relief admission); a 40-place day centre which will supplement the day hospital and offer flexible care up to 8 pm at night every day of the year; and a community resource centre where carers will be able to obtain information, advice and practical help. The two remaining wards at Hellingly will eventually be transferred to the DMHE. One of these is a 25-bedded unit and will provide longstay (though not necessarily permanent) care for very active and aggressive, organically-ill patients who cannot be managed elsewhere. The other is a 20-bed short-term admission and assessment ward which Dr Venkateswarlu believes is necessary in order to be able to assess, offer emergency help, give time to sort out placements and treat functional illness. It is a resource which he thinks should be available, though the better the service, the less it will be needed.

There is considerable informal contact between both consultants and Kilncroft because Padgett encourages them to bring visitors to see the home. He is felt to be unusual amongst private proprietors in that he takes trouble to get to know the consultants and their staff and is good at creating a sense of partnership with them. There has, however, been little need for professional input into Kilncroft, though a great deal of support is offered by the DMHE to SSD homes which have a very high level of both organically and functionally-ill residents.

In general, the availability of the hugely expanded private sector is welcomed by both consultants in that it offers variety and enables people to be placed where they are most likely to settle. 'SSD homes don't specialise—you can't pick and choose a home which will be right for a pacifist vegetarian or a beer drinker who is given to blue jokes.' Standards in private care do vary greatly, but tribute was paid to the quality of the work of the SSD registration officer for private residential homes.

Social services
Social services have recently gone over to a 'patch system' with team managers whose role is purely managerial. Previously, principal social workers had both management and clinical responsibility. Dr Irvine sees the result as weakening his SSD contacts at senior level and regrets the lack of trained social work support available to elderly people in the patch teams. In the psychogeriatric field, once an elderly person has been labelled as 'psychiatric', responsiblity tends to be passed on entirely to the DMHE team, apart from support by an excellent home help service. Social workers in the area tend to disapprove of use of the private sector and avoid referrals to it. In view of this combination of factors, no contact was made with the SSD in Hastings.

Summary
Kilncroft has much to recommend it. There is genuine and deep concern to provide a high quality of care, and the professional approach to management involved in its association with the

Croft group of homes minimises overheads and relieves care staff of time-consuming clerical and accountancy work. Compared with much specialist care reviewed in this study, the quality of the environment is domestic and pleasant, and the quality of care certainly no lower. But like the other private sector homes described in this study, Kilncroft does illustrate the difficulties of providing specialist care in converted domestic housing. Shared bedrooms, cramped lounges, narrow passages and the ubiquitous stairs give a sense of cramped and restrained conditions, in spite of the spacious built-on dining room. It is therefore of interest that the next home in the Croft group will be purpose-built, single storey and planned on the group unit principle. Since the visit was made steps have been taken to set up staff induction training and weekly in-service lecture sessions. There is also the beginning of a key worker system in the activities programme with one staff member taking regular responsibility for a small group over a four-week period. Steps are also being taken at Kilncroft to subdivide residents into two ability groups, while those who are severely physically disabled will be moved next door into a property which has just been acquired for use as a nursing home wing. It will be of interest to see how far these developments affect the approach to management described in the report.

R & M HOMES (REFERRED TO IN THIS REPORT AS OXFORD ROAD)
31 Oxford Road, Birkdale, Southport PR8 2EG:
Tel–Southport 64177
Proprietors: Roger and Margaret Alcock

Principal characteristics
This three-storey private nursing home, which was registered for 30 beds at the time of the visit, adjoins a private residential home under the same ownership. A link unit between the homes, which will provide another nine beds, is under construction. The home specialises in the care of dementia sufferers, though some patients suffering from personality disorder and severe communication problems arising from physical disability are also admitted, and it is heavily used as a source of longstay places by the local psychiatric hospital. Roger Alcock, the proprietor, is qualified as an RMN/RNMH. The establishment is a rare example of a private mental nursing home specialising in this field and it also illustrates many of the problems of offering private nursing care in converted domestic housing for this client group.

History
The proprietors were originally interested in setting up a home for mentally handicapped people, but were advised that the elderly mentally infirm were in the greatest need. They first established the residential home at 33 Oxford Road, but when the adjoining property became available, decided to develop it as a nursing home, so that they could take patients who were profoundly confused, and share the administration, catering and other costs. The nursing home was opened in 1984 with ten beds, and registration was extended to 30 when alterations were completed in April 1985. Both houses have extensive gardens at the rear and it is hoped to build on these to provide day care, relief care and sheltered flats.

Design and furnishing
The nursing home is a large detached Edwardian town house in a quiet residential street half a mile from the centre of Southport—an attractive seaside resort which, in its heyday, attracted holiday-makers and retired industrialists from the Merseyside

conurbation. The building is on three floors, plus an underground basement which is used for staff rooms and storage. Entrance is via a zig-zag ramp, replacing a steep flight of steps, to the (locked) front door. The entrance passage leads to a lounge, two two-bedded and one four-bedded bedrooms, and a WC and bathroom, medical treatment room, nursing office and kitchen. A short flight of stairs leads downwards to a large room built out at the back which is currently used as a lounge and dining area, but will be primarily used for games and activities when the extension is completed. A lift and gated stairs provide access to the upper floors which each provide three two-bedded rooms, one three-bedded room and one four-bedded room. There are no single bedrooms. Each bedroom has its own lavatory cubicle and there is a bathroom with an easi-bath on each floor. There is also a lavatory cubicle and shower built into the corner of the large lounge. The extension linking the two homes (under construction at the time of the visit) will provide two moderate-sized rooms to be used as lounge and dining space respectively, plus a passage-way between the two homes and bedroom accommodation on the two upper floors. The proprietor and his secretary have a crowded but well-equipped office near the top of the building.

Much care has been taken over decoration, especially in the smaller lounge, which has an elaborate flock wallpaper and ornate plaster ceiling. There are fine mantlepieces throughout the building and bedroom walls are decorated in an unusual rough-plaster finish. The building is carpeted throughout with the exception of the large lounge, which has a parquet floor, and the spaces directly underneath the beds, which are vinyl covered. Furnishing in bedrooms, however, consists only of duvet covered beds and cupboard/shelf units. There are no chairs and no dressing tables, since it is felt that these would serve no useful purpose, but some photographs and ornaments are displayed on mantlepieces. There is also no provision for screening personal areas within each room and even the toilet cubicles allow little space for assistance with the door closed. Thus, while spacious and pleasant, the effect is not private or homely, and this is seen as inevitable when caring for severely demented patients.

Gates across the bottom and top of both flights of stairs prevent any access to bedrooms during the day in the interest of safety and, as will be noted below, residents are, at present, dressed and undressed downstairs so the bedrooms are quite literally sleeping quarters. The lounges are furnished with chairs and settees covered in maroon-coloured vinyl together with occasional tables in the small lounge and plastic-topped square tables and upright chairs in the large lounge. There is access to the garden from the large lounge, but this, like the room itself, is only accessible to those who can manage stairs. Both accessibility and space on the ground floor and lower ground floor thus leave a good deal to be desired, while the upper floors are not used in the daytime—another illustration of the difficulty of using converted housing for this client group. An experimental alarm system which has been patented is attached to each bed. This notifies staff when the bed is vacated or wetted, and, as is noted below, it is hoped that this will not only alert staff to people who are restless or distressed but also help to promote continence. The system is, however, not yet robust enough for the use being made of it and is being further researched and developed.

Philosophy

The letterhead of the home describes it as a 'mental nursing home for the elderly confused and mentally ill with physical disabilities' and its statement on the 'aims of patient care' says that:

'it exists to promote and maintain the physical and mental well-being of all its patients. Both mentally and generally trained nurses are on duty 24 hours a day, to provide a high degree of nursing care. Care is based on individual assessment of each patient and takes into account any mental and/or physical infirmities they may have. The home is also visited, at regular intervals, by its own hairdresser, dentist, chiropodist, optician and physiotherapist.

Every patient is encouraged to be as independent as his/her condition allows, and the staff strive to maintain each individual's self-respect and dignity. Memory loss and confusion can become a problem in the elderly, so each patient is actively encouraged to participate in recreational and diversional therapies. Reality orientation groups are held by our trained staff to keep the patient in touch with normal daily life.

As 'our home' is the 'patients' home', we welcome visits by relatives and friends. Small personal items such as pictures and ornaments can be brought in, and will be arranged in the patient's room to create a homely atmosphere ...

When the time comes, every effort is made to ensure a peaceful and dignified end to life, and our aim is to provide continuous care until this time. Relatives may, if they wish, stay at the patient's bedside day or night, but if not, any deterioration in condition would be notified immediately.'

The home occasionally provides care for people with psychotic illness but, for the sake of other patients, cannot accept severe aggression. Any level of physical disability can be coped with and patients are cared for until death.

Ability range of residents
The average for the 29 patients in residence at the time of the visit on the CRBRS scale was 6.8, but there was a wide distribution in terms of severity with roughly a quarter (eight) of the patients being only mildly demented (scores 4 and 5) half (13) moderately so (scores 6–8) and a quarter (eight) with severe dementia (9–11). However, some of those with relatively mild memory impairment suffer from various types of personality disorder, delusional states, and hysterical outbursts and in some of them communication skills vary according to mood. One resident is blind and deaf, one is blind, and about ten are chair-bound. There is, therefore, a severe level of physical dependence and the proprietor estimates that 90 per cent of the job is providing physical nursing care.

Staffing
Staff levels
Daytime care staff levels are relatively high with an average of 26.4 hours per resident week. A considerable proportion of staff members are employed part-time. An overlap in the afternoon (between 2 pm and 4 pm) enables staff to take part in activities and one-to-one contact. It is intended that eventually the 'hotel side' of the undertaking—domestics, kitchen, laundry, and so on—will provide a 'third arm', with someone specifically employed to take charge of this section, which is not seen as sharing in the 'care' task. A full-time secretary is employed.

Staff qualifications and training
The proprietor is RMN/RNMH trained and as he usually sleeps on the premises he often provides the RMN staff cover which, as the brochure notes, is available at all times. Three other RMNs are employed at present, one of whom (the proprietor's brother-in-law) has clinical responsibility for running the home and appointing care staff. The owners would like to be able to appoint additional RMN staff which would enable the proprietor to take more time off duty; at present he feels unable to go away for

more than an occasional day's holiday. Seven SENs are also employed (three of these cover night duty).

Southport and Formby HA is unusual in that the training officer at Greaves Hall Hospital (which combines mental handicap, mental illness and psychogeriatric assessment care and treatment) invites the private sector to send staff to relevant parts of the five-day course he has devised for the induction and continuation training of nurses and nursing assistants. They are also invited to send staff to particular workshops on relevant subjects such as incontinence and drug abuse (nursing homes being vulnerable to the theft of drugs and syringes). Similar invitations are issued by his counterpart in charge of general nursing training at the Infirmary. Programmes relating to these courses and study days are circulated to the specialist private sector by the proprietor, who has taken on the role of co-ordinator of training, and who sees that his own staff make full use of the facilities available.

The Authority is also unusual in the close interest which it takes in monitoring and maintaining the quality of private nursing home care, and the nursing homes registration officer holds a 'matrons' meeting' every two months at which issues of common concern are discussed. In addition to facilities provided by the NHS, the proprietor is planning to provide his own in-house training course using bought-in professional tutors on a sessional basis, and inviting other homes and SSD to take part. (He did not however, expect SSD staff to be enthusiastic about using the private sector in this way.) At a more senior level the local technical college has organised courses for owners and managers and senior staff of private homes in association with the SSD and the Rest Homes Association, but these are not focused particularly on service provision for the elderly mentally ill.

Staff communication
Apart from ordinary handover sessions and weekly reviews (see below) there are no formal communication sessions at present, but staff evidently have the means to make suggestions and ensure they are taken up. It was staff disquiet at patients' long wait for breakfast, for example, which caused the experimental change in the getting-up routine discussed below.

Regime
Getting up and going to bed
Just before the visit was made, the routine had been changed

and residents are now brought downstairs in their dressing-gowns and given breakfast by the night staff. They are then washed and dressed by day care staff when they come on duty at 8 am. Before this, staff had to wake people at 5.30 am in order to get them dressed by 8 am, and breakfast was served by the day care staff. This was felt to be too early a start and too long a gap between the evening meal at 5 pm and breakfast. However, an early start is still required and on the day of the visit everyone was down by 7 am and had started breakfast. This was said to be exceptionally early because it had been a quiet night. Some patients in the small lounge went back to sleep in their chairs in spite of TV AM. After breakfast staff bring clothes down from residents' rooms and wash and dress them in the small washroom off the large lounge and in the treatment room next to the small lounge. This process was still going on at 9.45 am on the day of the visit.

The same process is reversed at night when staff bring down armfuls of night- and dressing-gowns after tea at 5 pm and change patients downstairs. People start going to bed after hot drinks are served at 8.30 pm and on the day of the visit everyone was in bed by 9.45 pm. No one was asked if they would like to stay up later, since it was presumed that they would be ready for bed after a long day and that patients with this degree of mental disability could not judge for themselves when they should go to bed.

Meals
Until the new dining room is completed, more physically-able residents who can manage stairs are served meals in the large lounge, sitting at tables for four and grouped according to ability, restlessness, etc. Those who are too disabled to manage stairs have meals on side-tables placed in front of their chairs in the small lounge. Most of these require a good deal of assistance. Breakfast consists of Weetabix or Redibrek with hot milk (served on alternate days), toast with jam, and tea. A two-course lunch is served ready-plated at 12.30 (to offer choice is considered to be impractical) and a cooked tea is provided at 5 pm.

Arrangements for meals were certainly unsatisfactory at the time of the visit but when the new dining room is completed it will be possible to serve all the patients in it, except for a small group who will sit at a table in the front lounge.

Activities
Daily group activities are arranged in the large lounge between

236

2 and 4 pm. This includes RO with the six or eight most able patients which is led by a care assistant who has had some previous experience in this field. Other activities include simple games, quizzes, use of picture cards and so on. A qualified physiotherapist attends the home for two sessions a week; one session is used for group exercises and games while the other focuses on individual treatment and assessment. A social therapist is employed to lead a singing and dancing session on Friday afternoons. Staff overlap during this period is intended to leave three people available to lead or help in activities. It is hoped that the proposed in-service staff training will enable them to be more skilled in their techniques (see above). However, at present these activities are only available to residents who are mobile enough to reach the large lounge and, as this will continue to be the 'games' room, this restriction seems likely to continue.

Bathing
A bath book is kept, allocating particular patients to particular days. Baths are usually given once a week, unless they are required more often. All patients have a morning 'strip wash' but the facilities for this in the cubicle adjoining the WC in the large lounge, where most patients are washed and dressed, are very limited. The recently installed easi-baths are said to make bathing much easier and more pleasant for both patients and staff.

Management of continence
By day: Incontinence pads are worn routinely by most patients during the day, but a book is kept recording toiletting and whether the patient was wet or dry, and an attempt is made to work out a pattern which will enable each patient to keep dry.

By night: A similar record is kept to enable patients to be got up when required rather than as a routine. The home is also using an experimental alarm system which is attached to each bed and notifies the staff when a patient is wet or gets up (see above). It is hoped that this will enable a more accurate pin-pointing of the time of individual need to micturate and so improve staff ability to take appropriate action.

Reviews
All patients are reviewed weekly by the RMN and general trained SEN nurse on duty; sometimes a care assistant is also present. The review is based on a 'patient care plan' in a chart form. This lists 'incontinence', 'diet', 'mobility', 'hygiene', 'group activity',

'relatives' co-operation' and 'additional concerns', and has columns headed 'action taken', 'observation' and 'evaluation'. The system had only just been started at the time of the visit and, on the record looked at, remarks in the 'action column' were limited to comments such as 'two-hourly toiletting', 'needs feeding', 'full care needed', while the sections relating to 'group activity', 'relatives' co-operation' and 'additional concerns' were blank, as were the 'observation' and 'evaluation' columns. Considerable progress is said to have been made since then in this regard.

If a patient had recently been admitted or was presenting management difficulties, a review would take place daily. A clinical review of all patients is undertaken not less than every three months in conjunction with the responsible GP and a case review with relatives is offered every six months to discuss general progress.

Personal allowance
In accordance with the recommendations of *Home life*, the brochure says that the proprietors will not arrange to collect pensions, bank money or make appointees for DHSS or other payments unless there is no-one else available to accept responsibility. Personal allowances are therefore usually managed by relatives and there is concern that in some cases they are being used to 'top up' the fees paid by social security so that the patient has no personal money at all available for his use. An account is kept for each patient which records withdrawals and deposits of petty cash. No specific assistance is given to patients in spending their personal allowance.

Involvement with relatives
The brochure explains the system of six-month case reviews and sets out the complaints procedure to be followed if relatives are unhappy about any aspect of patient care. There is no room available for private conversation between relatives and patients. Visiting at reasonable times is unrestricted, and one elderly husband often comes at lunch time and is provided with a free meal. There is no relatives' group or League of Friends, although there is awareness of the emotional problems of relatives and considerable effort is made to meet these, especially during terminal illness when patients are brought to a ground-floor room and relatives are encouraged to spend as much time with them as they want. The proprietor says he would like staff to be trained in caring in terminal illness.

Admission and assessment procedures
Except in an emergency, referral usually comes via the Greaves
Hall Hospital social worker. If the referral sounds suitable the
proprietor and a senior staff member visit the patient in hospital
to make their own assessment of physical and mental suitability
and, as far as possible, complete an assessment/record form. Apart
from the usual data, this gives (limited) space to topics such as:
patient's understanding of reason for admission to home; patient's
understanding of medical care and treatment; relatives' understanding and expectations; visiting problems regarding relatives/
friends; social activities; previous occupation; religious beliefs;
and hobbies. Habits relating to sleep, hygiene, mobility, communication and other aspects of personal and health care are
covered in considerable detail. Details which cannot be obtained
before admission are filled in later with the help of relatives and
from observation. If the patient is considered acceptable, relatives
are invited to inspect the home and discuss terms and conditions.
Before admitting a patient the home requires the discharging
hospital doctor and social worker to sign a declaration stating
that the patient needs the level of care provided in a home
specialising in the care of the elderly mentally infirm. Apart from
validating any claim for special DHSS rates, this declaration will,
the proprietor hopes, give him a defence against any charge of
illegally restricting personal liberty, for example by locking the
front door.

No home visit is made if the patient is admitted from hospital
and the records examined give minimal information about previous home conditions. However, an effort has been made to
obtain old photographs and use them to stimulate memory and
some knowledge of the patient's past is obtained in conversation
with relatives. There is, however, no formalised system which
ensures that this information is obtained. The social history
passed on via the hospital system may be extremely sketchy, and
no medical history or information, apart from current medication,
is given to the proprietor who finds this lack of information a
serious handicap.

Professional and support services
Statutory services
As has been noted, the local psychiatric hospital, Greaves Hall,
combines mental handicap, psychogeriatric and acute psychiatric
patients. The psychogeriatric section is staffed by one and a half
consultants, six CPNs and a social worker and has available

three 28-bedded wards and a day hospital. It is hoped to open a fourth ward shortly which will enable better differentiation between treatment of functional illness and dementia. There has been an unusual tradition of close co-operation between the psychogeriatric team, Sefton SSD and the private sector, which is reflected in the establishment of a number of specialist homes in the private sector. The consultant interviewed uses specialist residential homes to cope with people whose memory impairment is sufficient to cause lack of orientation, but who are free from severe behaviour problems or serious physical disability; he would expect the Oxford Road nursing home to cope success-fully with additional behaviour problems and physical disability. If the dementia is so severe that the patient is not thought to have any perception of quality of life and the level of dependency is very high, longstay hospital care—either at Greaves Hall or at Winick Psychiatric Hospital (where the HA still has some beds) is arranged if this is felt to be more appropriate. It is clear that the psychiatrist and social worker see the specialist residen-tial homes and the Oxford Road Nursing home almost as satellites of Greaves Hall. They have detailed knowledge of what the staff in each could and would cope with and they are willing to provide an immediate response to a request for help, and to take back a patient placed in a home if he cannot be managed.

The CPN team is at present hospital-based and directed, though some of its members would like it to become a service in its own right, based in a family support/counselling advisory centre, and with direct access to emergency and relief beds.

This close connection between the statutory and private sector is reflected in the exceptional amount of attention given by the HA to the registration and supervision of nursing homes. New applicants are required to purchase and study a pack of relevant literature costing £25 and there is a careful process of interview and assessment before applicants are approved. Current policy is not to register new nursing homes for more than 25 beds unless there are very exceptional circumstances. The ideal number is considered to be between 16 and 18, since less than 14 is not financially viable, and more than 20 becomes institutional. Any nursing home which admits people with a diagnosis of dementia is required to register as a *mental* nursing home and have an RMN on duty or on call at all times. Ordinary nursing homes which continue to care for people who develop dementia are permitted to do so, although the proportion of such patients, the severity of their illness and the staff's capacity to cope is closely scrutinised.

As a result of the close co-operation between the SSD and the HA, joint visits have been paid by the two registration officers, not only to the six specialist private residential homes but also to Sefton SSD's own 36-bedded specialist home and to the Oxford Road nursing home. The joint report, written as a result of these visits, is discussed further on page 22.

None of the statutory service providers seem to be concerned at the explosion of private care in the area, although there are now 124 registered homes (in all categories) in Sefton, and 87 new applications pending. About 25 per cent of their residents (500 people) are 'immigrants' from outside the borough. The view taken by the Assistant Director for Social Services is that 'this figure is peanuts' when compared to the whole elderly population, and that immigrant residents probably make fewer demands on services than people living in their own homes. The availability of private beds is seen as making it possible for both health and social services to cope. Nevertheless, there are plans to make an existing SSD home in the south of the borough into a specialist, joint-funded establishment which will be managed by social services but staffed by both nursing and social services personnel and supported by visiting para-medical professionals. There are also plans for a 36-place day unit to be attached to the existing EMI home.

General practitioner
Patients in Oxford Road may retain their own GP if they wish, and about a third have done so. The rest are looked after by one GP who, at his suggestion, visits weekly to discuss non-urgent clinical matters but is available at any time.

District nursing service
All nursing procedures are undertaken by staff, and the district nurse is not involved.

Other services
Physiotherapy, chiropody and hairdressing are provided in the home. Physiotherapy is included in the basic fee, but other services are charged as extras. The proprietor would like registered rest homes to club together to employ relevant professionals on a full-time basis and share their use between homes, but this has not yet proved to be practicable.

Summary

The higher fees available from the DHSS to patients in nursing homes together with the availability of dual registration and less insistence on single rooms in the nursing home sector, seem likely to encourage a considerable increase in specialist nursing home care. Oxford Road offers an interesting indication of the advantages and disadvantages of this form of provision. As the private residential homes discussed in this report have illustrated, the use of town houses with limited ground floor accommodation present serious problems in providing a sufficient area for the movement and activity of residents, and the need to service the capital costs of private care makes it difficult to offer sufficient care at fees which can be afforded. This is especially true if, as is current policy in Southport and Formby HA, new homes are not registered for more than 25 beds. Stresses are likely to arise between the nursing model of care and the desire to maintain independence and as normal a lifestyle as possible. Some of the constraints on high-quality care in the nursing home field are inescapable within the present legal and fiscal framework, but others are susceptible to changes in the quality, status, attitudes and training of the staff, so the development of the Oxford Road home over the next few years will be a matter of considerable interest.

WILLIAMWOOD HOUSE
Strathay Avenue, Netherlee, Glasgow:
Tel–Glasgow 637 1168

Principal characteristics
At the time of the visit Williamwood was the only residential home in Scotland to specialise in the care of elderly people with mental disability and one of the very few *voluntary* homes in the whole of the UK which specialises in this way. It provides 30 places for people suffering from moderate dementia or from other forms of mental illness and it places strong emphasis on individualised care, normal lifestyle, rehabilitation and high activity levels. The sponsoring organisation is the Church of Scotland and there is an overtly Christian focus in the home's management. The Church of Scotland is now planning two more homes on the same lines and much interest in the management and regime has been shown by the statutory sector in Scotland.

History
The Board of Social Responsibility for the Church of Scotland, under its Director, Frank Gibson, had become increasingly concerned at the lack of appropriate provision in Scotland for people suffering from dementia and the reluctance of local authorities to become involved in this field. The opportunity to provide a specialist home came when the Church of Scotland was bequeathed a pleasant two-storey mansion with extensive grounds in a fashionable part of Glasgow. The sale of the land made it possible to add a bedroom extension and equip and furnish the building to a high level. The total cost was more than one million pounds. The home was opened in the middle of 1983.

Design and furnishing
The main building is a solid, two-storey, stone mansion, built in the 1930s. An imposing central doorway (always unlocked during the day) leads into a wide passage which runs the full width of the house and leads to the dining and kitchen area on the left side, and three spacious lounges on the right. Immediately opposite the entrance is a large room, separated from the passage

by a clear glass screen. This room is used as an office and staff room, and is the hub of the building, with constant coming and going by both staff and residents. The upper floor of the main house provides a staff flat for the OIC and two spare rooms for visiting relatives and students. The new bedroom wing matches the style of the original building and is also on two floors, though because of a fall in the ground its upper storey is level with the ground floor of the main house. It is built on a 'race track' design with 18 single and six double rooms round the perimeter and bathrooms, laundry and kitchenettes in the middle. The entrance landings on both floors are used as extra sitting areas and one corner has been made into an excellent residents' telephone room which is glassed in and has comfortable seating. The quality of furniture and furnishing throughout is of a really high standard, and, with the possible exception of Bemerton Lodge, is better than in any home included in this study. However, residents are encouraged to furnish their own rooms if they wish to do so. No bed-sitting rooms are locked during the day and residents are encouraged to make as much use of them as they like, though not many do so.

The grounds are not secure but egress is via a short drive leading into a side road and residents do not often reach the main road without being observed by neighbours and encouraged to return. No attempt is made to prevent residents from entering or leaving the building. During the visit one resident repeatedly walked out of the front door, round the house and back through the French window into the office.

Ability range of residents

The CRBRS range was 1–8 with an average of 5.7. About half the residents scored 7 or 8 and could therefore be classed as severely confused, but no one was without considerable residual capabilities. The point must again be made that these scores do not enable poor performance arising from dementia to be distinguished from poor performance arising from lack of stimulation: it may therefore be that these scores would be higher in other institutions. However, the psychiatrist involved in the admission process does not consider very severely demented people to be suitable for the regime or able to benefit from it. The emphasis is rather on caring for people with different mental disabilities which range from a resident with an early vascular dementia combined with an acute anxiety state (but still able to read and knit) to a resident with an aristocratic personality who had suffered from localised brain damage and had almost become a longstay hospital patient because of faeces-smearing, stripping and compulsive food-stealing, but who has proved manageable by means of rewarding co-operation with a daily glass of sherry (in a Church of Scotland home!). Various residents suffer from severe depressive and anxiety states. Most residents are mobile with assistance and only one has so far been found unmanageable; a man who had 'beserk fits' during which he laid about staff and residents with a fire extinguisher.

Philosophy

An official statement says:

> 'The whole thrust of the philosophy of the running of the home is towards reorientation, rehabilitation, and care. The appointment and training of staff has been done with this in mind and a programme for daily living is being developed within which it is hoped to reawaken dormant interests and abilities which will assist in the whole process of providing a better level of living for each individual resident.'

'Rehabilitation', as the primary objective of care, is strongly emphasised by the OIC and, at the time of the visit, four residents suffering from depression and anxiety were in the process of being prepared for transfer to non-specialist homes. There is, however, a potential conflict here since staff are engaged in encouraging residents to exercise all their faculties as fully as possible in 'their home', but if they are too successful it may cease to be their home. Williamwood is Christian in its ethos. There is a daily service in which residents are encouraged to take part and the daily staff meeting includes prayer and spiritual reading.

Staffing
Staff levels

In theory there are four care staff and a senior on duty during the day time, giving a ratio of only 14.1 care staff hours per resident week (if one assumes that the senior does not provide personal care).

In practice, however, it is difficult to maintain even this level owing to staff sickness and holidays, and senior staff are often involved in direct care-giving, to the detriment of their management responsibilities. A letter from the line manager written a year after the home was opened draws the board's attention to this situation, and to the extra demands on staff arising from time needed for training, carrying out key worker roles, organising activities, relating to visiting professionals and students, and developing Williamwood's wider role as a resource centre. He urges that the staffing levels should be reviewed.

Staff qualifications and training
A substantial amount of planning and consultation took place before Williamwood House was set up and the philosophy for staff training was clear before any appointments were made. The staff spent some months training together before the home was opened under the supervision of the board's training officer and, together with the residential social work supervisor, she continues to provide important input and support. The OIC has both RMN and CSS qualifications, the latter being obtained on secondment by the Board as part of the preparation for opening the home. The other senior staff are a young woman with CQSW training and a middle-aged male SRN, since it is felt the senior staff should be mixed in age, sex and type of experience, and should share their roles and administrative tasks. A similar effort has been made to mix age, sex and experience (as in a normal household) in the care staff. More than 200 people applied for jobs when the home was opened and there was a major problem in selection. The OIC, John Wyllie was looking for people who would not have preconceptions about the task: 'the home was going to be different so the staff needed to be different'. There was some initial concern that elderly female residents would mind receiving care from young men, but in the event the residents seem to accept care from male staff in the same way as they accept a male doctor. There has also been no complaint from relatives on this score.

A great deal of effort is put into in-service training. All staff are given a loose-leaf hand book/procedure book which is added to from time to time. It includes: an outline of the duty of all staff; admissions procedure; list of items for new residents; task allocation/responsibility; health and safety at work; communication; key/additional and supervisors list; missing residents; on call procedure; complaints procedures; monies held in home on behalf of resident; medical procedure; accident/incident procedure; lifting residents; renewals and repairs procedure; mail; meetings; toiletting.

To give one example of the detailed nature of the contents:

Communication

1. Make sure the resident can hear what you say

2. Try to communicate without background noise or disturbance

3. Be clear, short and to the point in your speech

4. Face and speak directly to the resident

5. Always allow time for your message to register

6. Remember: there is a whole range of differences between you and the resident

7. Do not use jargon, keep it plain and simple

8. Local terms may be used, if you do not understand it ask

9. Remember the non-verbal communications/they are often very much more expressive

10. Always use the resident's preferred name ... Do not speak down to the resident

11. Listen to what is being said. Try to differentiate fact from fiction

12. If resident is agitated never argue, try to distract

13. Try not to concur with talk you know to be untrue

14. When the resident is being realistic show and say this

15. Any disorientated talk can be often diverted to an area which gave pleasure in the past then the resident can be led to the reality of initial conversation

16. Convey interest, patience and your natural warmth in all conversations with residents.

There was a period of induction training before the home was opened and a rolling series of lectures is provided for staff appointed since then. These include topics such as: the aims of the home; the nature of residential care work; mental illness in old age; physical aspects of care; social work practice; team work; specific therapies; Christian aspects of the work; and relatives' involvement. There is also a regular training programme for all staff providing more detailed information on some of the topics listed above and additional items, together with visits to other residential homes, the local social services offices and the psychiatric hospital. All care staff have regular supervision sessions with a senior member of staff, as well as review sessions relating to the residents for whom they are particularly responsible. Staff are also encouraged to attend training seminars run by the Church's Board of Social Responsibility and to follow relevant Open University courses.

Staff communication
Apart from the formal training sessions noted above, all staff (including the cook, domestics and handyman) attend a daily staff meeting in the office at 2 pm at which the programme for the rest of the day is discussed, and responsibility for particular activities assigned. Management problems; physical health care; longer-term plans and other issues are also discussed. As was noted above, this meeting includes a short act of prayer and worship, though those who do not want to participate actively need not do so. The atmosphere is very informal with most staff members sitting on the floor. The early morning handover session is equally informal. It takes place on the landing leading to the bedroom wing, and includes an allocation of duties for the morning. It is often joined by residents who are already up. There is no general occurrence book but all events relating to particular residents are noted on separate pages which are kept in a loose-leaf file and are subsequently transferred to the resident's personal files, so a detailed running record on each individual is maintained.

Regime
Getting up and going to bed
Some residents get themselves up before the day staff come on duty at 8 am. Others are assisted according to known habits and needs based on the detailed information collected by the key worker. They then go to the dining room and are served with breakfast without delay. Those who wish to sleep late can do so. Going to bed is similarly a gradual process and several residents

were still up at 10.30 pm on the night of the visit. The key worker's checklist again breaks down the usual pattern and exact habits for each resident.

Meals

The dining area (two connecting rooms) resembles that of an attractive, homely hotel, with eight fully-laid tables, seating four people each, covered with bright table cloths. Milk, tea, sugar, vegetable dishes and so on are provided for each table. Staff and guests eat here at the same tables as the residents—an arrangement not found elsewhere in this study. A choice of dishes is always offered and, if the offer is not understood, the resident will be shown the dishes and asked to show a preference.

Mid-afternoon tea is served from a trolley in the main sitting room and there is supper in the dining room at 9 pm. Residents are encouraged to help the cook prepare meals and some residents take pride in clearing tables, washing up and putting crockery and cutlery away.

Activities

A summary review of the programme of care activities written a year after the house was opened states that 'All things are designed either to educate, or to recall past events in their lives.' It goes on to say:

'Recall activities are varied by the use of individual effort, by group sessions, the use of personal diaries and also by the use of monthly themes designed and researched by members of staff, with the use of visual aids, talks, and recall in which residents and their relatives are asked to to contribute material.'

On the day of the visit about half the residents took part in a religious service (held daily) and later there was a 'fashion show' with staff modelling dresses brought in on approval from a local shop, and encouraging residents to select those which they liked. In the afternoon some residents played darts and board games. Others sat in a separate lounge with quiet recorded music. One staff member was ambitiously attempting to paint a mural on the sitting room wall (nine months later its character had changed considerably but it was still incomplete). A physiotherapist (the cook's sister) came in to advise on exercises to help a resident who had recently returned from hospital treatment in a totally immobile state. There was also a lot of 'just sitting' which reflected the policy of trying not to over-organise or regiment residents.

Clothing
In common with most of the establishments reported in this study clothing is 'normal', dignified, and in accordance with the residents' tastes—but at Williamwood attention is also paid to make-up, jewellery, and other aspects of personal appearance. Relatives are provided with a detailed list of items for self care, care of clothing, writing letters and so on, which should be brought in with the resident. Unlike almost every other home reported in this study residents are encouraged to bring valuables with them. 'We insist that folk here have nice things to wear and wear them with pride.' Key workers are expected to recognise and keep track of the possessions of 'their residents', and relatives are encouraged to insure valuables and to take responsibility for washing woollens and delicate fabrics. The key worker's breakdown of 'lifestyle' includes very detailed questions about mode of dressing and undressing, care of teeth, use of cosmetics, usual hair care, and care of finger and toe nails.

Bathing
Baths are arranged on an individual basis according to need and preference. The key worker check list on this item starts:

'When is the known preference? How do you know this? Does resident know when they require a bath? Does resident say they are going for a bath? What prompting is needed for a bath? Is resident able to prepare items required for bath eg towels/soap/cloths/oils/talc/fresh clothing/dressing gown? If *yes* list all resident can do. If *no*, list all resident cannot do or what prompts are required.'

The check list goes on to analyse the whole bathing process in equal detail.

Management of continence
By day: Again the key worker provides a detailed breakdown of the abilities of each resident. The toileting process is unobtrusive but this is, of course, made much easier by the number of residents who are capable of self care or managing with minimal help. Pads are used if necessary but they are avoided as far as possible. Enemas are rarely required and are given by the district nurse.

By night: Night staff are encouraged to develop their own procedure based on the knowledge of the needs of each individual resident. Commodes are used as little as possible because they are thought to create a 'hospital atmosphere' and discourage use of WCs. At the time of the visit two were in use—one by the very disabled resident who had recently come back from hospital, and one by a resident who was dying.

Key worker system

Key workers at Williamwood do not have responsibility for providing ordinary personal care for 'their' residents; their role is rather a social one—arranging the admission; helping the resident to settle; making a 'pen portrait' of history and personality; providing the very detailed 'identification of indivi- dual lifestyle' described above; building up a relationship with the resident and relatives; acting as advocate in situations requiring this; and setting goals for improving the quality of life. Each key worker is backed by a 'support worker' on the opposite shift, who provides another avenue of relationship with the resident, helps the key worker in all the areas of intervention required, and helps to plan and implement the goal-setting process. A senior member of staff acts as supervisor and as instigator, advisor and guide for the key and support workers. He or she also has responsibility for planning review and support meetings and intervening in situations where the personalities concerned are incompatible or the key worker is becoming over-involved.

Reviews

During the first weeks of residence, major problems such as sleeping difficulties, incontinence and loss of daily living skills are identified, and detailed plans made to rectify them. At the end of the first month a review meeting is held, attended by the supervisor, key worker, support worker, and any other interested staff and, if appropriate, by relatives and the resident. At this meeting practicable goals are agreed, together with projected dates for achieving them. Thereafter reviews are three-monthly, but the key worker is expected to put a monthly report into the continuation files.

Personal allowance

Some residents are able to handle their personal allowance and everyone has some money in their possession. For some residents however, ability to use money may be part of the rehabilitation programme with defined goals in this regard. This is an area in which considerable work has been needed to change relatives' attitudes.

Outings
The home owns a minibus which is driven by a gardener/handyman who is an important member of the staff. Outings of one kind or another are a frequent event, but there are also more ambitious barbecues, sports events (staff versus relatives) and parties, sometimes using the facilities of the leisure centre or hiring a room in a hotel for an evening; such events involve staff, relatives, all patients, and local volunteers.

Involvement with relatives
As was noted above, a great deal of trouble is taken to bring relatives into the admission and review procedure and they are also encouraged to take as much part as they wish in the social and physical care of the resident. The message given is: 'tell us what part of the care of your mother/husband/wife/sister *you* want us to take over?' *not* 'this is what *we* will permit you to go on doing'. In addition, there is a relatives' committee which concerns itself with activities, such as those described above, but also discusses the therapeutic approach of the home with senior staff and acts as the core of a wider relatives' group. This is gradually being built up to include the families of day care and respite care attenders.

Volunteers
In common with other Church of Scotland homes, Williamwood has a local management committee which concerns itself with day-to-day issues and activities. Two members of this committee make a regular monthly visit of inspection and each member is allocated three residents who they get to know on a personal basis. 'Coffee mornings' are held at which committee members and residents mix on social terms. The committee also represents the home in the neighbourhood and helps to involve local residents in its affairs, and to allay fears about the lack of 'locking up'. Committee members and other volunteers help with fund-raising events, and may also help in giving personal care. The WRVS run the home's shop.

Day care and respite care
When it was set up, Williamwood was intended to provide four shortstay beds. However, the need to 'decant' residents from

another home resulted in two of these beds becoming longstay, and one is needed for assessment, so only one is now available on a planned basis for respite care. This is primarily used to allow caring relatives to take a holiday as, although there is a heavy demand for weekend breaks, the cost acts as a deterrent. It is hoped that this use will increase as Williamwood becomes better known as a 'community resource'.

Day care was also operating on a very small scale at the time of the visit but it is hoped that eventually day care will be offered to six people every weekday.

Assessment and admission procedures

Applications for admission are made on a standard form to the Head Office of the Board of Social Responsibility of the Church of Scotland. The Board then obtains medical, social work and psychiatric reports. Collecting this information takes some time, and when it does arrive it is not always as detailed or as accurate as it might be. When the other paperwork is complete a member of the Williamwood staff makes a home visit and also writes a report. If the application still appears to be suitable it is put before an assessment panel consisting of a psychogeriatrician, two social services representatives, two representatives from Head Office and the OIC or his deputy. It was originally intended to have a nursing representative from the Health Board, but this was never achieved. The panel, which meets about every two months, is highly selective. Applicants are often turned down as being 'too good' or as 'not having been properly tried in a local authority home' or 'not properly assessed for domiciliary support'. 'It is not good enough', the psychogeriatrician says, 'for the social work report to state "this lady would benefit from Williamwood". Almost anyone would benefit from Williamwood. The question is does she need Williamwood?' Another problem is that people with mild or moderate confusional states who could be managed elsewhere are referred because the professionals do not believe that Williamwood can cope with severe disability. However, such referrals are sometimes appropriate since some people with moderate disability become totally demoralised by their experiences in the community and benefit from a stay in Williamwood as a staging post to ordinary residential care. The most successful admissions have been of people who would otherwise be in longstay hospital care because other homes would not take them. In considering suitability for

Williamwood, the panel also take account of the level of disability in the home at any particular time.

Professional support services
General practitioners
If the resident is within reach of her previous GP, this link is maintained. If not, she is added to the list of one of half a dozen local practices. This 'spreads the load' and enables working links with the local GPs to be used as a means of making William-wood's existence and ethos known. The rapport established with each practice differs but in general the GPs have been found to be interested and co-operative.

Psychogeriatric services
Williamwood draws its residents from all over Glasgow, and therefore from various hospital catchment areas, which continue to be responsible if further treatment is needed. However, Dr Anne Gray, based at Leverndale Hospital, has been involved in the project since its inception and provides continuing support on the admission panel and in any other way that is required. Dr Gray's CPN gives 'depot' injections if required and her registrars 'make themselves familiar' with what Williamwood has to offer, but she says 'John Wyllie is so good that he does not need help'. In general, the lack of common boundaries between psychiatric, geriatric and social services catchment areas makes co-operation and the pursuit of common policies very difficult, and the impression is that Williamwood is on the periphery of everyone's vision—not quite fitting in to any system: admired but not fully used or understood.

Social services
The SSD is under tremendous pressure in the operation of its own residential homes which are unsuitable in architectural terms, under-staffed, and trying to cope with a very difficult mix of physical disability, mental disability, former vagrants and so on. The senior social worker interviewed, felt that voluntary homes 'take the easier end of the market', thereby adding to the stigma of an SSD admission, and she expressed disquiet at the quality of care offered in some voluntary homes. (These are views which are strongly disputed by the Board's Director who says that recent statistics produced by the Social Work Services Group of the Scottish Office should have dispelled forever 'the myth that voluntary homes take the easier end of the market'.) She had, however, long had contact with Williamwood as a member of

254

the assessment panel and, in spite of her suspicion of both organised religion and voluntary homes, was very impressed by the quality of care it offered and the degree of disability with which its staff coped.

Summary
As the first home of its kind in Scotland, Williamwood House has aroused much interest, and the Church of Scotland's Board of Social Responsibility is to be congratulated on the care which was taken in setting up and equipping the project, and in training its staff. It is encouraging that it is planned to open two similar homes in 1987. However, there is a danger that service providers will avoid the challenge to follow Williamwood's example with such excuses as 'that's all very well but OICs of Wyllie's quality don't grow on trees'; 'but *we* don't have a million pounds to spend in setting up a home', 'but *they* are not really coping with severe dementia'; 'but *their* residents come from the posh end of the market'; and so on.

The Board believes strongly that its example *can* be followed and points out that both the capital costs and staffing levels of similar homes run by the Strathclyde Regional Council are higher than those of the Board. They also point out that staff familiarity with the CRBRS rating scale may have produced a degree of under-scoring and that use of a scoring system which is focused on dementia does not reflect the level of other forms of psychiatric and behavioural disorder which are managed at Williamwood House. Although opinions differ on some of these issues, it is clear that Williamwood House represents an important initiative in the development of specialist care in Scotland and illustrates the potential role of voluntary organisations in the provision of specialist care—an example of good practice from which everyone working in this field can learn.

5 Conclusion

Key aspects of good practice

Design of homes
Design and location should reflect residents' need for:

1. Single-storey buildings.

2. Ample and safe space for indoor and outdoor walking.

3. Individual private rooms.

4. Easy orientation and identification of key facilities.

5. Minimal distance between sitting, dining, bedroom and lavatory provision.

6. Dignified, non-institutional furnishing and decoration with opportunity to furnish and decorate own rooms.

7. Kitchenette facilities.

8. Minimal boundaries between staff and resident 'territory'.

9. Discreet staff supervision.

10. Easy access to local shops.

11. Good transport facilities.

Promotion of individuality and choice
The regime should provide:

1. A detailed and 'illustrated' personal history for each resident.

2. A detailed account of previous lifestyle, tastes and habits.

3. Opportunity to bring in or acquire personal possessions, furniture and ornaments.

4. Appropriate use of surname and title.

5. Allocation of a key worker with responsibility for developing, maintaining and reviewing individual care plans.

6. Extensive opportunities for choice in relation to sleeping, eating, selection of clothing, use of personal money and other daily living activities.

7. Management of continence based on observed individual need.

8. Discrimination in the use of music and television.

9. Activities inside and outside the home which reinforce remaining abilities and are dignified and enjoyable.

10. Encouragement of continued social contacts and involvement of relatives in care-giving and decision-making.

11. Provision of emotional support for relatives.

Assessment and admission procedures
Assessment and admission procedures should ensure that:

1. Each prospective longstay resident receives full social, psychiatric and physical investigation.

2. Every appropriate effort has been made to maintain a viable home situation.

3. The decision to offer a place is based on a multi-disciplinary consensus which includes the OIC concerned.

4. The prospective resident and supporters are visited at home by a senior member of staff and the designated key worker in order to:

    a) arrange an exploratory visit to the home and (if appropriate) a trial stay;

    b) explain the philosophy and nature of the care provided, the admission procedures and the initial period of assessment;

    c) discuss the furniture, clothing and other personal possessions which the resident may wish to bring with her;

    d) begin to collect information about daily living habits and customs and a personal history.

(If the prospective resident is already in some form of care it will be even more important and more urgent to obtain as much information as possible about previous history and lifestyle and rescue any remaining possessions before the 'past' has vanished beyond recall.)

5. An agreed initial period of residence should be used as a trial stay during which no irrevocable steps are taken which would prevent a return to the previous domicile. During this time the key worker, aided by other staff should:

a) deepen personal contact with the resident and her supporters;

b) seek to minimise the disorienting and depressing effects of the move;

c) make a detailed record of behaviour and appropriate management using any tests which may be helpful and acceptable;

d) observe and report any potentially remediable causes of confusion and establish a realistic care plan.

6. At the end of the trial period the key worker should present her findings to a group which may include the resident herself, and should include relatives, senior staff and appropriate field-workers. The group should decide:

a) whether the placement is appropriate;

b) whether some more suitable alternative should be sought immediately;

c) whether it would be realistic to work towards rehabilitation and a change of domicile in the longer term.

If the resident's stay is to continue, the presentation should form the basis of a care plan which is reviewed at regular intervals.

Day care and respite care
If day care and respite care is provided, it is necessary to ensure that:

1. There are sufficient and well-placed sitting, dining, toilet and

other facilities so that temporary residents neither suffer nor cause distress and disturbance.

2. Staffing levels are high enough to cope with the extra workload and the additional administration, contact with relatives, home visiting and demand for emergency support which will be generated.

3. Provision of activity and occupation for the possibly more responsive day care and respite clients does not detract from the service offered to longstay residents.

Staffing
Senior staff
1. Candidates for appointment to senior positions should be required to show that they have: relevant skills and training; a real commitment to work with severe dementia sufferers; an interest in staff training and development; a desire for personal professional development.

2. OICs should have: opportunities to improve their professional competence; support from informed line management; regular professional consultation with a suitably-qualified adviser; sufficient clerical support.

3. OICs should be closely involved in decision-making processes relating to assessment and admission and in the development of the home as an integral part of wider service provision.

4. The OIC should maximise the opportunities offered to other senior staff to broaden their experience, carry delegated responsibility, share in the training of care staff and further their professional careers. Line management should provide full support in this.

Care staff
1. Care staff need to be provided at a level which makes possible the quality of care outlined above and also allows time for: training and supervision; inter-staff communication; good record-keeping; participation in assessment and admission procedures. This will normally demand a two-hour overlap of shifts every weekday.

2. The selection, salary, status and career opportunities for care

staff need to reflect the levels of skill and responsibility demanded of them.

3. A structured system of in-service training and day release training should ensure that all care staff receive a thorough grounding in all aspects of their task.

4. Care staff should routinely be involved in decision-making, forward-planning and problem solving within the home.

5. All care staff should receive regular individual and group supervision.

Domestic, catering, clerical, gardening and maintenance staff
All employees in the home, whatever their official roles, should be encouraged to contribute to the well-being of residents, interact with them and help them to take part in appropriate activities.

Urgent research and action
1. We need localised and detailed studies of the incidence of severe dementia with total loss of short-term memory or associated behavioural disorders so that realistic planning of specialist care for a given population can be undertaken.

2. The kind of longstay care offered and its cost to the user is, at present, often the accidental result of the initial mode of referral. We need information about the evaluation of 'pathways' to care followed by action to make the process equitable and the end result more appropriate.

3. There is general (though not universal) agreement that some dementia sufferers are too disruptive, aggressive or unco-operative to be given adequate care in a residential setting. However, we have little information as to the nature of the methods used to manage such people in a hospital ward and the reason why these methods cannot be used elsewhere. We need to know more about:

a) the number and prognosis of such patients;

b) the changes in building design, residential care staff levels and staff training which would be needed to manage them outside hospital;

c) The arguments for and against 'segregating' such people from less disturbed dementia sufferers.

4. Traditional routines of care-giving, combined with lack of delegation and training can result in an uneconomic use of staff and poor quality care. We need:

a) a detailed comparative study of various models of staff deployment;

b) a 'rule of thumb' method of calculating staffing levels which links staffing requirements to the demands of the physical environment, the physical and mental dependency of residents and the time required for training, management, admission procedures and other essential tasks.

5. The training of line managers, senior staff and care staff requires careful consideration and some standardisation. It needs to include:

a) in-service training packages on the lines of *Home ground* (see page xxiii);

b) rolling programmes of day-release courses aimed at staff with particular responsibilities and particular levels of experience which are open to all statutory and non-statutory care/nursing/ management staff within a particular locality;

c) a nationally-recognised professional qualification for specialists in this field which builds on and adds to either RMN or CSS/CQSW training.

DETAILED CHECK LIST USED IN THE STUDY

- Name of home
- Address
- Telephone number
- Officer-in-charge
- Date opened
- Category

General description
Residents
- Number
- Number longstay—average length of stay/number of new admissions each year
- Shortstay relief care: number of beds; average length of stay; usual frequency
- Beds available for crisis care—type of use; frequency
- Facilities for day care

Building
- Type
- Position
- Bedroom accommodation—shared/single; bedsitting
- Bathroom accommodation
- Lavatory accommodation—arrangement in relation to bedrooms; communal areas; facilities for assistance/wheelchair use
- Range and nature of communal rooms
- Garden access
- Transport availability
- Immediate environment
- Domesticity of atmosphere
- Design in relation to orientation/security/supervision/free movement

Range and level of disability among residents
- Physical
- Personality disorder
- Long-standing psychiatric illness
- Late-onset depression/paraphrenia
- Dementia
- Other
- Particular behaviour problems

'Philosophy' of the home
- Written statements of policy available?
- Views on risk/safety
- Segregation within the home
- Criteria for selection of clients
- Unacceptable categories
  a) on admission
  b) for on-going care
- Shared use of facilities and space between different groups

History—how and why set up as a specialist home

Management structure
- Source of ultimate authority re policy and procedures
- Relationship with OIC of home—contact/consultation/decision-making process
- Other important sources of influence (funding, professional influence etc)

Quality of life
Dignity
- Privacy—in toiletting, bathing, etc. Provision and control of private space in own bedrooms
- Furniture and possessions in own bedrooms
- Management of clothing
- Means of coping with incontinence—by day: by night
- Modes of address
- Staff knowledge of individual residents and their history
- Food service
- Choice of food
- Means of dealing with unpleasant eating habits
- Means of assisting residents at mealtimes

Risk management
- Means of surveillance—by day: by night
- Control of boundaries (locked doors, observation, layout of paths, electronic signals)
- Prevention of internal trespassing into staff quarters, other residents' rooms etc.
- Use of physical restraint (special chairs, fixed trays, cotsides etc)
- Policy in relation to smoking
- Policy in relation to handling kettles, etc.
- Features of particular interest

Relationships
- Contact, support, antagonism, friendship, etc between residents
- Relationship between residents and care staff (with particular emphasis on key worker relationships, if this system is used)
- Relationships with domestic, catering and handyman staff
- Family contact and ways of encouraging its maintenance
- Use of volunteers

Activity and self care
- Individual written programme
- Constant encouragement in self care tasks
- Use of basic reality orientation techniques
- Use of environment to promote orientation
- Encouragement in familiar household tasks
- Encouragement of other personal or group activity
- Encouragement of external activity (walks, shopping, bus rides, outings)

Rigidity and flexibility of timetable
- Getting up procedures
- Going to bed procedures
- Bathing procedures
- Eating arrangements
- Toiletting schedules
- Toleration of eccentric behaviour (with examples)
- Toleration of night-time wandering

Drugs and ordinary medical care
- GP arrangements
- GP referral and usual interview arrangements
- Handling of repeat prescriptions
- Drugs given at staff discretion
- Dispensing method
- Use of sedatives
- Use of other tranquillisers, anti-depressants etc.
- Procedure if client refuses to take drugs
- Responsibility for nursing procedures—enemas, catheter management, dressings etc

Staffing
Senior staff
- Description
- Roles
- Qualifications
- Grading

264

Care staff
- Description
- Roles
- Qualifications
- Grading and how paid

Domestic staff (including cook, handyman, laundress etc)
- Description
- Roles
- Involvement with care
- Grading and how paid

In-service training
- Secondment to outside courses
- Formal supervision sessions
- Group discussion
- Induction techniques

Professional procedures
Referral process
- Sources of referral
- Mode of referral
- Nature of physical assessment required
- Nature of psychiatric assessment required
- Nature of social assessment required
- Process of consultation with client and relatives
- Preliminary visits to home by client
- Preliminary visits to client's home by staff
- Any brochure available (get copy)

Admission procedures
- What signed consents/undertakings are completed by both parties
- Is there any check on the legal validity of this in relation to the client
- How is the actual admission usually managed
- What procedures if the client is reluctant to stay
- Arrangements for re-trial stay
- Procedure if unhappy or unsuitable

Procedures for deciding on long-term stay

Procedures for temporary absence
- To hospital
- On holiday

Procedures for discharge
- To hospital
- To other longstay care
- Likely reasons

Procedures relating to dying and death
- 'Philosophy' relating to care of the dying
- Access by relatives
- Use of additional nursing support
- Means of dealing with removal of the body, funeral arrangements, disposal of assets, communication of the news to residents

Any regular review system?
- If not, why not
- If so
  —Purpose
  —Procedure
  —Means of recording
  —Examples of outcome

External back-up—from the home's point of view
SSD
- Social work
- OT
- day care
- other

CPN service
- specialist
- general
- hospital or community-based

District nursing service (including supply of aids, incontinence pads etc)

Ancillary NHS support
- chiropody
- physiotherapy
- OT service
- specialist deaf and blind advice

Psychogeriatric/psychiatric service

Geriatric services

Other public services
- library
- education
- transport
- external day centre hospital

Bought-in services from private operators
- chiropody
- hairdressing
- private nursing

FERRARD FACT SHEET FOR DAILY LIVING

ROUTINES AND ATTITUDES

Rises about   am
Morning cuppa on waking [_____]
Beverage with or without milk, sugar, both
Milk [_____]   sugar [_____]   both [_____]
Attends to toilette before [_____]   after [_____]
breakfast
Required assistance [_____]

BREAKFAST, LUNCH AND TEA

Small appetite
Good appetite
No known dislikes
Requires special diet
Requires assistance

Morning paper
Cigarettes/pipe
Periodicals

PERSONAL ROUTINE ACTIVITIES AM

_____
_____
_____
_____

Choice of mid-morning beverages etc.

_____
_____
_____

LUNCH, DINNER

No known dislikes
Requires special diet
Dislikes are _____

_____
_____
_____

USUAL AFTERNOON ACTIVITIES

Shopping		Rests	
Walks dog		T.V.	
Visits friends		Radio	
Others		Gardens	

EVENING MEAL, TEA

Meal at_____pm

Dislikes_____

BEDTIME ROUTINE

Usual bedtime [   ] pm
Occasional early night [   ] pm
Baths in evening [   ]
Number of pillows [   ]
Sleeps well [   ]   needs sedation [   ]
Sleeps with night light [   ]

DISLIKES, FOOD AND ALLERGIES TO IT

Fruit _____

Veg. _____

Meat _____

Poultry _____

Fish _____

Beverages _____

Condiments _____

I am allergic to_____

Religious observance forbids_____

PRIVACY AND PERSONAL POSSESSIONS

Prefers single room [   ]
Willing to share [   ]
Expects provision for keeping personal items
safe and on display [   ]
Likes comfortable chair in room to enjoy
quiet afternoon rest/radio [   ]
                    letter writing [   ]
                    reading, knitting [   ]
                    others [   ]

Prefers personal gifts, goods, cigarettes
flowers, confectionery etc. to be shared
with others ☐
for self ☐
Will receive guests readily ☐
Will receive guests by consent ☐
Will receive guests by invitation only ☐
Everyone should knock and be invited in ☐

GENERAL HEALTH

State of health, good ☐
frail ☐
Eye-sight: good ☐
poor ☐
Hearing: good ☐
poor ☐
Disability_____
Incontinence—urine ☐ faeces ☐

PHYSICAL HEALTH

Special drugs e.g.
Iron   Insulin   Others

Details _____

Takes liquid medicines in tea etc. ☐
Tablets crushed in jam ☐
Sensitivity to drugs, others_____
_____
_____

PERSONAL HYGIENE

Interested and care with appearance ☐
Bathes—am, pm ☐
Wears dentures ☐
Pedicure—regular care given ☐
Hairdresser—regular ☐
Shampoo and set ☐
Perms ☐
Hair not cut—religious beliefs ☐
Special help is needed with _____

Requires assistance with general
toilette ☐

ACTIVITIES, OCCUPATIONS, LINKS WITH COMMUNITY

Member of society, group, organisation
Active Church go'er
W.I.
Bridge Club
Others
Favourite regular outdoor activities
Detail _____

_____

Day trips		Bingo	
Cinema		Whist	
Concerts		Bowls	
Walks		Golf	

Favourite T.V. programmes _____

Favourite radio programmes _____

SOCIAL NEEDS AND RELATIONSHIPS

Enjoys—Meeting others
Opportunity to discover their interests
and skills
Discuss pattern of their lives
Expects basic right for privacy as an
emotional need
Expects not to need to conceal emotions
Expects not to be denied emotional or
sexual needs
Expects not to be discouraged in formation
of close personal relationships
Enjoys talking about earliest family
life
Can relate family history
Can keep up to date with changes in—
Family relationships, births, deaths etc.
Keeps contact with long standing friends
Feels it important to discuss bereavement
of—self, friends, family

TERMINAL CARE

Last rites and counselling
Minister or Priest or Counselling
    Name _____
    Phone No. _____
Personal wishes eg
Family, friends in attendance etc.
Desired attitude at bedside—expand

_____

_____

FUNERAL ARRANGEMENTS

Responsible—Name _____
           Phone _____

REQUESTS

Private
Wreaths, flowers etc.
Cremation
Burial
Expand _____

CPA Policy Studies

Mental illness in old age: *meeting the challenge*
by Alison Norman
Policy Studies in Ageing No. 1

Mental illness in old age often provokes a sense of hopelessness amongst those who encounter it, be they the ill people themselves, their relatives, or staff in health and social services. Yet mental illness in late life is far from being a hopeless cause, as this study demonstrates. The kinds of mental illnesses encountered amongst older people are explained and the report describes many imaginative responses to the need for assessment, treatment and support for this vulnerable group. It is hoped that the book will stimulate all the helping professions—GP's, psychiatrists, social workers, nurses, residential and day care staff, and voluntary bodies—to look afresh at their policies and practices.

Age is opportunity: *education and older people*
by Eric Midwinter
Policy Studies in Ageing No. 2

Education and elderly people is a paradoxical issue. Despite the increased leisure time available to retired people, the numbers engaged in education drop dramatically. Yet education could provide older people with that kind of constructive and invigorating activity which offers positive enjoyment and prevents mental decline. This book argues strongly for a much more freewheeling and imaginative approach. It traces the current woeful state of provision, and compares that with the occasional illustrations of successful innovation. It also attacks the myth that "you can't teach an old dog new tricks", and claims that older people have the capacity, as well as the right to learn, and, just as important, the resources to help their fellows. The book calls on government, local authorities and voluntary agencies to assist the spread of self-help learning co-operatives among older people, along the lines of some of the University of the Third Age projects now under way. Penetrating analysis and practical recommendations are offered in this report for all those interested in promoting educational opportunities for elderly people and for those concerned to develop a thriving adult and continuing education service.

274

Triple jeopardy: *growing old in a second homeland*
by Alison Norman
Policy Studies in Ageing No. 3

Elderly people in the ethnic minorities in this country face a triple jeopardy. They are at risk through old age, through cultural and racial discrimination and through their lack of access to essential services, because of poor command of the language and conflicting religious and cultural practices. Their own communities do what they can to help, but their resources are limited, and sensitive provision of statutory services is essential to provide such people with services which *ought* to be available to everyone. These include health, housing and social services; residential and domiciliary care; library and adult education provision—and the simple opportunity to meet for recreation and relaxation with people of their own age and culture.

Triple jeopardy looks in detail at the issues involved in service provision by both statutory and voluntary agencies, and it suggests practical action which can be taken immediately to improve matters.

The wage of retirement: *the case for a new pensions policy*
by Eric Midwinter
Policy Studies in Ageing No. 4

Pensions in Britain are no more generous than they were in Victorian times, when 'outdoor relief' was paid to old people in need. At less than one third of the average wage, state pensions are still provided at subsistence levels. Retired people are, as a result, socially excluded from society as a whole, unable to enjoy the kind of lifestyle most people take for granted.

This report, however, is more than a critique of present pension levels: it presents the case for a radical overhaul of the social security system which provides this income support. In place of the contributory pension it proposes a single retirement wage, payable to all on the basis of citizenship alone, and suggests the replacement of national insurance by taxation to fund the social security system. Fundamentally, it argues that *non-work* is as important to society as is *work*, and that retirement should not, therefore, carry a financial penalty. Based on official Department of Employment Family Expenditure Surveys, it calculates what people need to *spend* in order to participate in an averagely-comfortable lifestyle—put at £80 a week in 1985 (revised to £90 in 1987). Moreover, the study demonstrates that this is in fact a solution that the nation *can* afford, if it so chooses.

Councils of care: *planning a local government strategy for older people*
by Alan Norton, Bryan Stoten and Hedley Taylor
Policy Studies in Ageing No. 5

This report reviews those local government policies which affect older
people and argues that the growth in the absolute number of the retired
population, and the particular demands which frail elderly people make
on the social services, necessitate a reappraisal of their approach by local
authorities. In spite of the financial constraints imposed by central
government policy, realistic options are still available to achieve desired
ends.

The report examines the extent to which mainstream services such as
leisure and recreation, adult education and environmental planning can
be more effectively geared to maintaining the quality of life of the
majority of older people, and considers the most cost-effective ways of
meeting the specialised health and welfare needs of the minority of very
frail persons. The study concludes with a discussion of the need for
greater co-ordination between departments within the same local
authority as well as between agencies, to ensure maximum use and
distribution of existing resources.

Growing old together: *elderly owner-occupiers and their housing*
by Hedley Taylor
Policy Studies in Ageing No. 6

Over 90 per cent of elderly people continue to live in their own homes
until they die. Over half of these are owner-occupiers, who are now
growing old along with their housing. Many of their properties are in
an unsatisfactory condition, and their owners are faced with considering
costly repairs and alterations, or with moving to somewhere easier to
maintain.

Growing old together considers the wide range of help available to
both those who stay put and those who decide to move on. It examines
the existing range of provision and identifies gaps in it, explores how
the various options should be made more widely available to those
who might benefit from them, and assesses their likely effectiveness in
meeting the needs of elderly owner-occupiers over the next 20 years.

CPA Reports

The CPA Report Series includes the following titles:

Home help: *key issues in service provision*
by Rodney Hedley and Alison Norman
CPA Reports No. 1

The hospice movement in Britain: *its role and its future*
by Hedley Taylor
CPA Reports No. 2

Continuing care communities: *a viable option in Britain?*
by David Hearnden
CPA Reports No. 3

Bricks and mortals: *design and lifestyle in old people's homes*
by Alison Norman
CPA Reports No. 4

Going places: *two experiments in voluntary transport*
by Rodney Hedley and Alison Norman
CPA Reports No. 5

Co-ordinating housing and social services: *from good intentions to good practice*
by David Hearnden
CPA Reports No. 6

Not a nine-to-five job: *staffing and management in private and voluntary residential care homes*
by Terri Donovan and Deirdre Wynne-Harley
CPA Reports No. 7

Caring for cash: *the issue of private domiciliary care*
by Eric Midwinter
CPA Reports No. 8

Further information on these and other publications and services may be obtained from the Centre for Policy on Ageing, 25–31 Ironmonger Row, London EC1V 3QP, telephone 01 253 1787.